Wynn Kapit • Lawrence M. Elson

The Anatomy Coloring Book

a benefit for amta Student members

american **massage therapy** association®

Custom Edition

Taken from:
The Anatomy Coloring Book, Third Edition
by Wynn Kapit and Lawrence M. Elson

D1495444

Cover illustration by Wynn Kapit. Cover design by Pam Byers for American Massage Therapy Association.

Taken from:

The Anatomy Coloring Book, Third Edition
by Wynn Kapit and Lawrence M. Elson
Copyright © 2002 by Wynn Kapit and Lawrence M. Elson
Published by Benjamin Cummings
A Pearson Education Company
Glenview, IL 60025

This special edition published in cooperation with Pearson Learning Solutions.

Pearson Learning Solutions, 501 Boylston Street, Suite 900, Boston, MA 02116
A Pearson Education Company
www.pearsoned.com

Printed in the United States of America

4 16

000200010271935221

JH

ISBN 10: 1-323-00697-4
ISBN 13: 978-1-323-00697-9

american **massage therapy** association®

welcome to **AMTA**

The American Massage Therapy Association is the largest non-profit, member-driven association with the strongest benefits in the profession.

Your AMTA Student Membership

Start your education off on the right foot with the resources you need to be successful in the classroom and in your career.

- Liability insurance for school-sponsored activities
- Mentoring Program
- Local chapter to connect with massage therapists in your area
- E-newsletters providing timely industry news, updates and tips
- AMTA Job Bank
- Career Guidance Center

Explore the AMTA website and learn more about all the resources available to you during your schooling and as you begin your career!

amtamassage.org/student

877.905.2700

the **amta path**

Enjoy **broad liability insurance** throughout your career **and** receive benefits specific to your stage of practice.

AMTA Student membership

what you need to excel in school

liability insurance for school-sponsored activities
study aids
mentoring
test prep

AMTA Graduate membership

what you need to launch your practice

general liability insurance
discounts on products & services
free resume posting
career guidance
mtj subscription

AMTA Professional membership

what you need to build long-term success

general liability insurance
best continuing education
free marketing for your practice
local chapter
AMTA Job Bank
Find a Massage Therapist® locator service
mtj subscription

Once you have graduated from your program, take the next step by **renewing as a Graduate member** at amtamassage.org!

Congratulations on joining thousands of other massage therapists who have built their careers with **the only national non-profit massage association** by their side!

amtamassage.org

how to **use this book**

Welcome to an innovative and fun way to study anatomy! In this special **AMTA Student member** version of the *The Anatomy Coloring Book*, you'll find illustrations specifically chosen for their application to massage therapy.

Coloring is a playful approach to study. And play delivers a wide array of learning benefits! While stimulating the brain (making you more likely to remember what you study), it simultaneously reduces stress, increases focus, and draws upon your innate creativity.

Ready to get started? Here's how it works…

Gather your colored pencils

It is best to have at least 10 felt-tipped pens or colored pencils (no crayons). Colored pencils are more versatile because you can lighten or darken each color. Felt-tipped pens produce bright colors. If you purchase your colors individually (as opposed to a set) you should primarily choose light colors, but be sure to include gray and black.

Tip: Most art stores carry high quality colored pencils sold individually. Start your search there, or look for less expensive sets online!

Get ready to color

This simple six-point coloring system will get you the best results:

1. **Watch for dark outlines** — These are the parts of the illustration that need to be colored. These are also identified by small letters (A, B, C, etc.).

2. **Use titles as your key** — Each title has outlined letters followed by its letter label. (A, B, C). Color a title and then its respective part with the same color.

3. **Change colors for the next title/part** — For best results, do not use that color again on a different part/title on that plate. (If you run out of colors, you may have to repeat.)

4. **Use the same color on related parts** — Whenever you see a superscript (A1, A2), these parts of the illustration are related to each other. Use the same color for these.

5. **When there's a dash, only color the title** —When you see a small letter label followed by a dash (A-, B-) only color the title or heading. These do not refer to a specific part of the illustration.

6. **Watch for these special symbols and color accordingly:**
    -   Asterisk (✷) — Color these areas or words gray.
    -   Black circle (•) — Color these areas black.
    -   Don't color sign (⋰) — Don't color these areas at all.

Legend of symbols used throughout the book

⋰	Don't color
✷	Color gray
•	Color black
N.S.	Not shown
	A broken outline represents one form lying underneath or behind another
	The subject matter is microsopic in size

following best **coloring practices**

Although coloring seems straightforward (after all, we all colored as kids!), there is a method to using this book. Here are some tips:

- **Start with CN** — Right before each illustration, you'll find the initials CN for coloring notes. Read these first! You'll learn which colors to use and what to notice as you color.

- **First things first** — Look at the list of titles and start with the first one. Locate the part it refers to (the letter labels – A, B, C – can help), choose a color and get coloring. Start with the title and then color the corresponding part.

- **Don't skip around** — Color the items in the order that they are presented on the page. They are usually listed in that order for specific reasons.

- **Think light for large** — Reserve your lightest colors for the largest areas to be colored. A dark color on a larger part of an illustration may dominate the plate.

- **Do what's natural** — You might want to use the colors traditionally associated with certain structures of the body:
  - **Red** for arteries
  - **Blue** for veins
  - **Purple** for capillaries
  - **Yellow** for nerves
  - **Green** for lymphatics
  - **Note:** *When you color a diverse group of structures (i.e. many arteries or veins), you'll need to use more than one representative color.*

Get the most from your learning experience

Each illustration has explanatory notes and titles that can help you in your studies. Be sure to use these to multiply the value you get from this book!

- **Read the corresponding note first** —Then, as you color, go back over the information in your mind. Try talking through the information out loud as you color, as if you were explaining it to another student.

- **Test yourself on the titles** — The titles are usually placed away from the illustration to facilitate your review. Try covering them when testing your recall of the information.

Tip: Form a small study group and then let them in on the fun. Take turns coloring in the different parts of an illustration, while quizzing each other on the parts.

Be sure to tell your friends how they can get their own *Anatomy Coloring Book* and many other career-boosting benefits through AMTA Student membership!

Abbreviations

In the text and titles, the following abbreviations may precede or follow the names of the structures identified, e.g., Post. auricular m., Brachial a., Scalenus med. m.:

A. = Artery	Lig. = Ligament	Post. = Posterior
Ant. = Anterior	M., Ms. = Muscle(s)	Sup. = Superior, superficial
Br. = Branch	Med. (preceding term) = Medial	Sys. = System
Inf. = Inferior	Med. (after term) = Medius	Tr. = Tract
Lat. = Lateral	N. = Nerve	V. = Vein

ABOUT THE AUTHORS

WYNN KAPIT

Wynn Kapit, the designer and illustrator of this book, has had careers in law, graphic and advertising design, painting, and teaching.

In 1955, he graduated from law school, with honors, from the University of Miami and was admitted to the Florida Bar. He practiced law both before and after military service. Four years later, he decided to pursue a childhood ambition and enrolled at what is now the Art Center College in Los Angeles, where he studied graphic design. Afterwards, he worked in the New York advertising world for six years as a designer and art director. He "dropped out" in the late 60s, returned to California, and began painting. His numerous exhibitions included a one-man show at the California Palace of the Legion of Honor in 1968. He returned to school and received a Masters in painting from the University of California at Berkeley in 1972.

Kapit was teaching figure drawing in Adult Ed in San Francisco in 1975 when he decided he needed to learn more about bones and muscles. He enrolled in Dr. Elson's anatomy class at San Francisco City College. While he was a student, he created the word and illustration coloring format that seemed to be a remarkably effective way of learning the subject. He showed some layouts to Dr. Elson and indicated his intention to do a coloring book on bones and muscles for artists. Immediately recognizing the potential of this method, Dr. Elson encouraged Kapit to do a "complete" coloring book on anatomy and offered to collaborate on the project. The first edition of *The Anatomy Coloring Book* was published in 1977, and its immediate success inspired the development of a completely new field of publishing: educational coloring books.

Kapit went on to create *The Physiology Coloring Book* with the assistance of two professors who were teaching at Berkeley: Dr. Robert A. Macey and Dr. Esmail Meisami. That book was published in 1987 and has gone through two editions. In the early '90s, Kapit wrote and designed *The Geography Coloring Book*, now in its second edition.

LAWRENCE M. ELSON

Lawrence M. Elson, Ph.D., planned the content and organization, provided sketches, and wrote the text for the book. This is his seventh text, having authored *It's Your Body* and *The Zoology Coloring Book* and co-authored *The Human Brain Coloring Book* and *The Microbiology Coloring Book*. He received his B.A. in zoology and pre-med at the University of California at Berkeley and continued there to receive his Ph.D. in human anatomy. Dr. Elson was assistant professor of anatomy at Baylor College of Medicine in Houston, participated in the development of the Physician's Assistant Program, lectured and taught dissection and anatomy at the University of California Medical School in San Francisco, and taught general anatomy at City College of San Francisco.

In his younger days, Dr. Elson trained to become a naval aviator and went on to fly dive-bombers off aircraft carriers in the Western Pacific. While attending college and graduate school, he remained in the Naval Air Reserve and flew antisubmarine patrol planes and helicopters. His last position in his 20-year Navy career was as commanding officer of a reserve antisubmarine helicopter squadron. He continues to fly his own airplane for business and pleasure.

Currently, Dr. Elson is a consultant and lecturer on the anatomic bases and mechanics of injury, a practice that has taken him throughout the United States and Canada. He has testified in hundreds of personal injury trials and arbitrations. His research interests are focused on the anatomic bases and mechanisms of injury.

To report errors or make suggestions to enhance the effectiveness of this book, Dr. Elson can be contacted at: foranat@earthlink.net.

DEDICATION

For my wife, Lauren, and sons, Neil and Eliot.

WYNN KAPIT

My work in this book is dedicated to my incredibly talented and loving wife Ellyn, and my family: Jennifer, Chris and Gina, Amelia and Bill, Bill and Chris, Aunt Boo, Hilary and Jim, Jason, Jodi, Stephanie, and all living extensions of the remarkable Elson, Stembel, Green, Kornblau, and Gilberg families... and especially to Andrea, who made it happen.

LARRY ELSON

TABLE OF CONTENTS

NERVOUS SYSTEM

CENTRAL NERVOUS SYSTEM

PERIPHERAL NERVOUS SYSTEM

AUTONOMIC OR VISCERAL NERVOUS SYSTEM

CARDIOVASCULAR SYSTEM

ANATOMIC PLANES & SECTIONS

MEDIAN A

The median plane is the midline longitudinal plane dividing the head and torso into right and left halves. The presence of the sectioned midline of the vertebral column and spinal cord is characteristic of this plane. The median plane is the middle sagittal (mid-sagittal) plane.

SAGITTAL B

The sagittal plane is a longitudinal plane dividing the head and torso into left and right parts (not halves). It is parallel to the median (not medial) plane.

CORONAL, FRONTAL C

The coronal or frontal plane is a longitudinal plane dividing the body (head, torso, limbs) or its parts into front and back halves or parts.

TRANSVERSE, CROSS D

The transverse plane divides the body into upper and lower halves or parts (cross sectons). It is perpendicular to the longitudinal planes. Transverse planes may be horizontal planes of the upright body. Transverse planes are called "axial" or "transaxial" sections/slices by radiologists.

CN: (1) Use your lightest colors on A–D. (2) Color a body plane in the center diagram; then color its title, related sectional view, and the sectioned body example. (3) Color everything within the dark outlines of the sectional views.

Study of the human body requires visualization of internal regions and parts. Dissection (dis, apart; sect-, cut) is the term given to preparing the body for internal inspection. One method of dissection permits consistent visual orientation by cutting the body into parts, called "sections," along the lines of reference, called "planes." The viewing and study of internal human structure in these planes is possible through medical imaging, such as computerized tomography (CT) and magnetic resonance imaging (MRI).

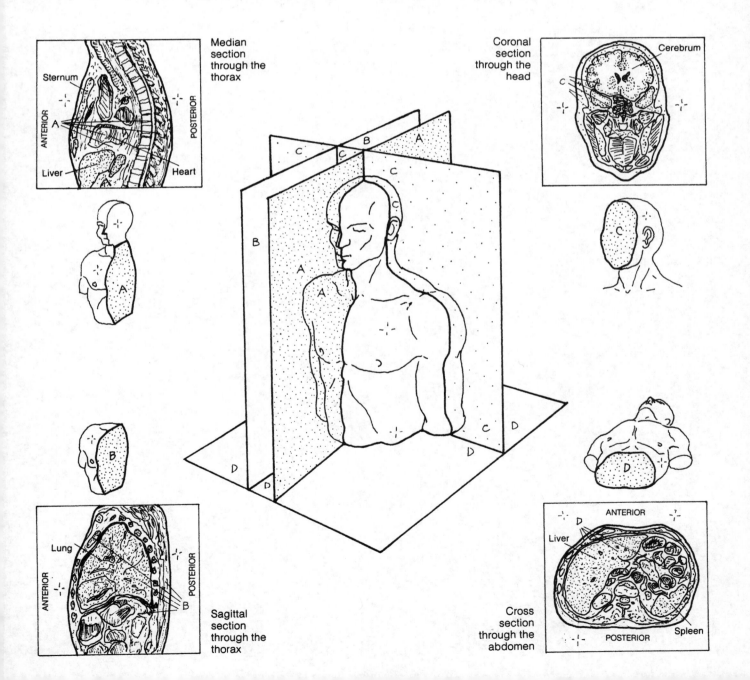

Median section through the thorax

Sternum

ANTERIOR

POSTERIOR

Liver

Heart

Coronal section through the head

Cerebrum

C

Sagittal section through the thorax

Lung

ANTERIOR

POSTERIOR

B

Cross section through the abdomen

ANTERIOR

D

Liver

Spleen

POSTERIOR

TERMS OF POSITION & DIRECTION

CN: Color the arrows and titles, but not the illustrations.

Terms of position and direction describe the relationship of one organ to another, usually along one of the three body planes illustrated in the previous plate. To avoid confusion, these terms are related to the standard anatomical position: body standing erect, limbs extended, palms of the hands forward.

CRANIAL, SUPERIOR, ROSTRAL A

These terms refer to a structure being closer to the head or higher than another structure of the body. These terms are not used with respect to the limbs.

ANTERIOR, VENTRAL B

These terms refer to a structure being more in front than another structure in the body. The term "anterior" is preferred.

POSTERIOR, DORSAL C

These terms refer to a structure being more in back than another structure in the body. The term "posterior" is preferred.

MEDIAL D

This term refers to a structure that is closer to the median plane than another structure in the body. "Medial" is not synonymous with "median."

LATERAL E

This term refers to a structure that is further away from the median plane than another structure in the body.

PROXIMAL F

Employed only with reference to the limbs, this term refers to a structure being closer to the median plane or root of the limb than another structure in the limb.

DISTAL G

Employed only with reference to the limbs, this term refers to a structure being further away from the median plane or the root of the limb than another structure in the limb.

CAUDAL, INFERIOR H

These terms refer to a structure being closer to the feet or the lower part of the body than another structure in the body. These terms are not used with respect to the limbs.

SUPERFICIAL I DEEP J

The term "superficial" is synonymous with external, the term "deep" with internal. Related to the reference point on the chest wall, a structure closer to the surface of the body is superficial; a structure further away from the surface is deep.

IPSILATERAL K CONTRALATERAL L

The term "ipsilateral" means "on the same side" (in this case, as the reference point); "contralateral" means "on the opposite side" (of the reference point).

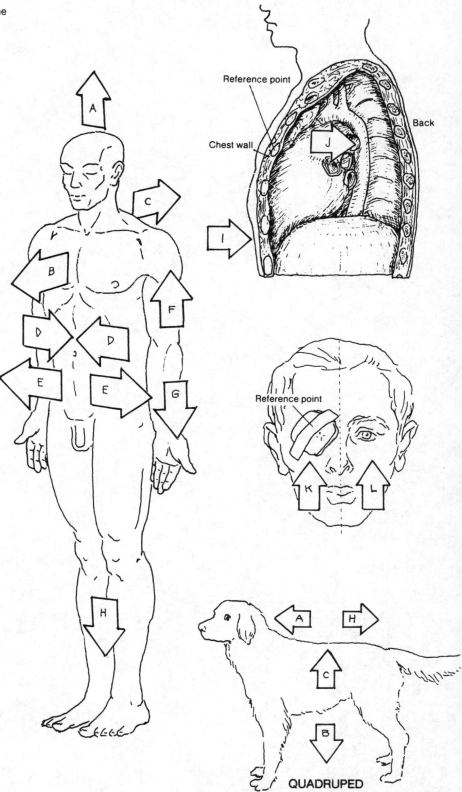

The quadruped presents four points of direction: head end (cranial), tail end (caudal), belly side (ventral), back side (dorsal). In the biped (e.g., human), the ventral side is also anterior, the dorsal side is also posterior, the cranial end is also superior, and the caudal end is inferior.

SYSTEMS OF THE BODY (1)

CN: Use light colors. Color the skeleton (A). Color the musculature (B) brown. Color the major arteries and heart red (with darker outlines), veins blue (C). Color all lymphatic vessels (D) green. Color nerves, brain and spinal cord (E), yellow. Color the insets representing the endocrine system (F). Pick a skin color for the integumentary system (G). Note that the latter two are independent systems, but are graphically combined here in one body.

Collections of similar cells constitute tissues. The four basic tissues are integrated into body wall and visceral structures/organs. A *system* is a collection of organs and structures sharing a common function. Organs and structures of a single system occupy diverse regions in the body and are not necessarily grouped together.

SKELETAL_A ARTICULAR_A'

The skeletal system consists of the skeleton of bones and their periosteum, and the ligaments that secure the bones at joints. By extension, this system could include the varied fasciae that ensheath the body wall/skeletal muscles and contribute to the body's structural stability. The *articular system* comprises the joints, both movable and fixed, and the related structures, including joint capsules, synovial membranes, and discs/menisci.

MUSCULAR_B

The muscular system includes the skeletal muscles that move the skeleton, the face, and other structures and give form to the body; the cardiac muscle of the heart walls; and the smooth muscle of the walls of viscera and vessels and in the skin.

CARDIOVASCULAR_C

The cardiovascular system consists of the four-chambered heart, arteries conducting blood to the tissues, capillaries through which nutrients, gases, and molecular material pass to and from the tissues, and veins returning blood from the tissues to the heart. Broadly interpreted, the cardiovascular system includes the lymphatic system.

LYMPHATIC_D

The lymphatic system is a system of vessels assisting the veins in recovering the body's tissue fluids and returning them to the heart. The body is about 60% water, and the veins alone are generally incapable of meeting the demands of tissue drainage. Lymph nodes, which filter lymph, are located throughout the body

NERVOUS_E

The nervous system consists of impulse-generating/conducting tissue organized into a central nervous system (brain and spinal cord) and a peripheral nervous system (nerves), which includes the visceral (autonomic) nervous system involved in involuntary "fight or flight" and vegetative responses.

ENDOCRINE_F

The endocrine system consists of glands that secrete chemical agents (hormones) into the tissue fluids and blood, affecting the function of multiple areas of the body. Many of these glands are under some control by the brain (hypothalamus). Hormones help maintain balanced metabolic functions in many of the body's systems.

INTEGUMENTARY_G

The integumentary system is the skin, replete with glands, sensory receptors, vessels, immune cells and antibodies, and layers of cells and keratin that resist environmental factors harmful to the body.

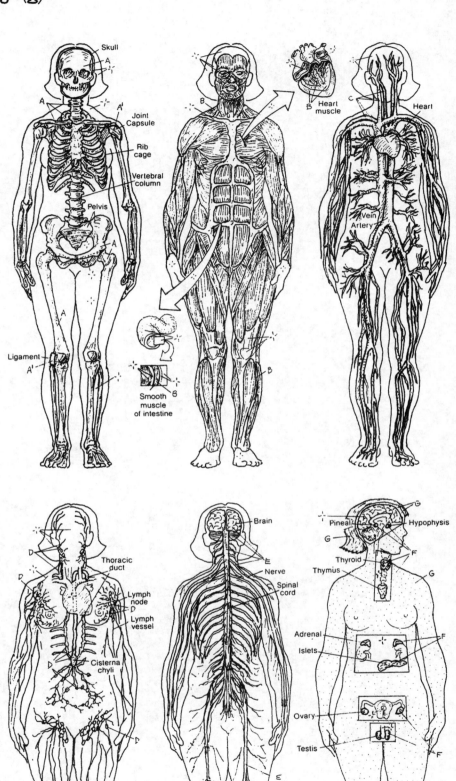

Skull
Joint Capsule
Rib cage
Vertebral column
Pelvis
Ligament
Smooth muscle of intestine
Heart muscle
Vein
Artery
Heart
Thoracic duct
Lymph node
Lymph vessel
Cisterna chyli
Brain
Nerve
Spinal cord
Pineal
Hypophysis
Thyroid
Thymus
Adrenal
Islets
Ovary
Testis

SYSTEMS OF THE BODY (2)

CN: Use different light colors from those used on the preceding plate.

RESPIRATORY H

The respiratory system consists of the upper (nose through larynx) and lower respiratory tract (trachea through the air spaces of the lungs). Most of the tract is airway; only the air spaces (alveoli) and very small bronchioles exchange gases between alveoli and the lung capillaries.

DIGESTIVE I

The digestive system is concerned with the breakdown, digestion, and assimilation of food as well as excretion of the residua. Its tract begins with the mouth and continues down to the abdomen, wherein it takes a convoluted course to open again at the anus. Associated glands include the liver, the pancreas, and the biliary system (gall bladder and related ducts).

URINARY J

The urinary system is concerned with the conservation of water and maintenance of a neutral acid-base balance in the body fluids. The kidneys are the main functionaries of this system; residual fluid (urine) is excreted through ureters to the urinary bladder for retention and discharged to the outside through the urethra.

IMMUNE / LYMPHOID K

The lymphoid system consists of organs concerned with body defense: thymus, bone marrow, spleen, lymph nodes, tonsils, and smaller aggregates of lymphoid tissue. This system, including a diffuse arrangement of immune-related cells throughout the body, is concerned with resistance to invasive microorganisms and the removal of damaged or otherwise abnormal cells.

FEMALE REPRODUCTIVE L

The female reproductive system is concerned with the secretion of sex hormones, production and transportation of germ cells (ova), receipt and transport of male germ cells to the fertilization site, maintenance of the developing embryo/fetus, and initial sustenance of the newborn.

MALE REPRODUCTIVE M

The male reproductive system is concerned with the secretion of male sex hormones, formation and maintenance of germ cells (sperm), and transport of germ cells to the female genital tract.

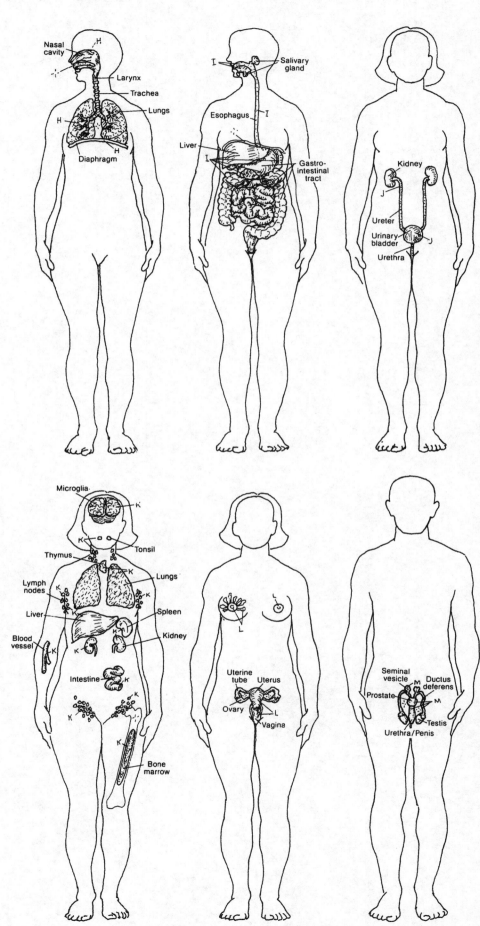

See 6

REGIONS OF THE BODY (ANTERIOR)

CN: The text for this and the next plate is located on the next plate. (1) The anterior/lateral regions have been grouped according to larger areas: e.g., head, neck. The regions of each area (A^1, A^2, etc.) all receive a single color. Color a title and the arrow pointing to its region. (2) Although the title "pudendal" (D-) is to be colored, that region, consisting of the female external genitals, is not shown (N.S.). The same is true for the perineum (D-), that region between the pubis and the coccyx, below the pelvic floor.

HEAD A-
  FRONTAL A^1 (forehead)
  TEMPORAL A^2 (temple)
  ORBITAL A^3 (eye, cavity/walls)
  NASAL A^4 (nose, cavity/walls)
  BUCCAL A^5 (cheek)
  ORAL A^6 (mouth cavity)
  MANDIBULAR A^7 (lower jaw)

NECK B-
  ANTERIOR CERVICAL B^1 (front of neck)
  LATERAL CERVICAL B^2 (side of neck)
  SUPRACLAVICULAR B^3 (above clavicle)

THORAX C-
  PECTORAL C^1 (anterior chest)

ABDOMINOPELVIC D-
  ABDOMINAL D^1 (abdomen)
  INGUINAL D^2 (groin)
  PELVIC D^3 (pelvis)
  PUBIC D^4 (genital region)
  GENITAL D^5 (reproductive organs)
    PUDENDAL D- N.S. (female genitals)
  PERINEAL D- N.S. (between pubis and coccyx)

UPPER LIMB E-
  DELTOID E^1 (shoulder/upper arm)
  AXILLARY E^2 (armpit)
  BRACHIAL E^3 (arm)
  ANTECUBITAL E^4 (front of elbow)
  ANTEBRACHIAL E^5 (forearm)
  CARPAL E^6 (wrist)
  HAND: PALMAR E^7 (palm)
  HAND: DIGITAL E^8 (fingers)

LOWER LIMB F-
  COXAL F^1 (hip)
  FEMORAL F^2 (thigh)
  PATELLAR F^3 (knee cap)
  CRURAL F^4 (leg)
  FIBULAR F^5 (lateral leg)
  TARSAL F^6 (ankle)
  FOOT: DORSUM F^7 (top)
  FOOT: DIGITAL F^8 (toes)

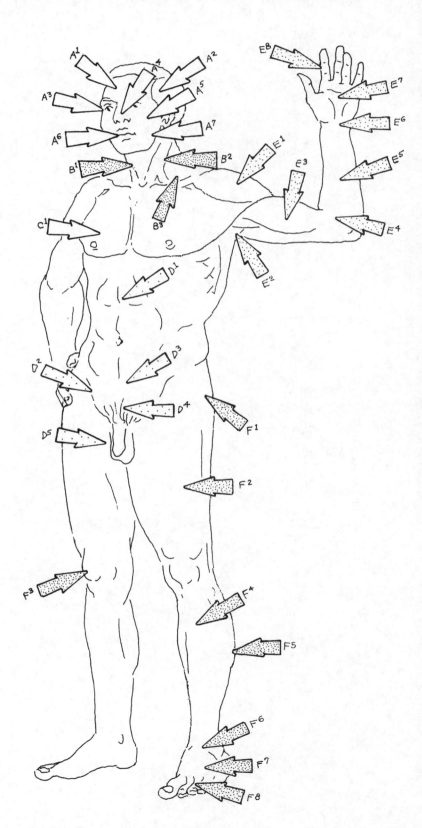

REGIONS OF THE BODY (POSTERIOR)

CN: (1) Use the same colors for divisions marked A, B, E, and F that were used for those letters on the preceding plate.

Regional anatomy is the organization of human structure by regions. Here are shown the major regions within the principal areas of the body (e.g., head, neck). There are many regions within regions, each of which includes structures from different systems, such as bone, muscles, blood vessels, and nerves. Study of the body by dissection is generally accomplished region by region. An in-depth regional awareness of human structure is fundamental for most health care providers.

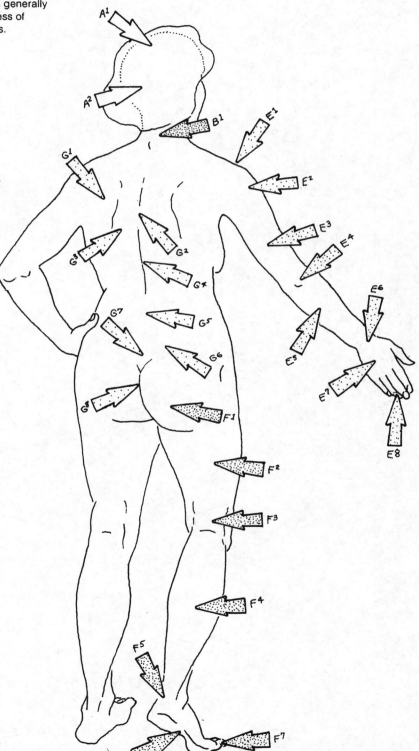

HEAD A-
PARIETAL A¹ (top and sides of head)
OCCIPITAL A² (back of head)

NECK B-
POST. CERVICAL /NUCHAL B' (back of neck)

BACK G-
SCAPULAR G¹ (shoulder blade)
VERTEBRAL G² (spinal column)
PARASPINAL G³ (along side spinal column)
THORACIC G⁴ (posterior chest)
LUMBAR G⁵ (lower back)
SACROILIAC G⁶ (vertebro-pelvic joint)
SACRAL G⁷ (posterior pelvis)
COCCYGEAL G⁸ ("tail bone")

UPPER LIMB E-
ACROMIAL E¹ (top of shoulder)
DELTOID E² (shoulder/upper arm)
BRACHIAL E³ (arm)
CUBITAL E⁴ (elbow)
ANTEBRACHIAL E⁵ (forearm)
CARPAL E⁶ (wrist)
HAND: DORSAL E⁷ (back of hand)
HAND: DIGITAL E⁸ (fingers)

LOWER LIMB F-
GLUTEAL F¹ (buttock)
FEMORAL F² (thigh)
POPLITEAL F³ (back of knee)
CRURAL F⁴ (leg)
TARSAL F⁵ (ankle)
FOOT: PLANTAR F⁶ (sole)
FOOT: DIGITAL F⁷ (toes)

CAVITIES & LININGS

CN: Except for H, use light colors. (1) Note that the linings for closed body cavities A¹*–D¹*) are to be colored gray. (2) In the open visceral cavities shown below, the linings receive the color (H).

CLOSED BODY CAVITIES

CRANIAL A **DURA MATER** A'*
VERTEBRAL B **DURA MATER** B'*
THORACIC C **PLEURA** C'*
ABDOMINOPELVIC D **PERITONEUM** D'*

Closed body cavities (The *cranial, vertebral, thoracic,* and *abdomino-pelvic* cavities) are not open to the outside of the body. Though organs may pass through them or exist in them, the organs' cavities do not open into these closed cavities. Closed body cavities are lined with a membrane: the thick *dura mater* in the skull and vertebral cavity, the thin, watery (serous) membranes (serosa) in the thoracic and abdomi-nopelvic cavities.

The cranial cavity is occupied by the brain and its coverings, cranial nerves, and blood vessels. The bony walls of the cranial cavity are lined by the dura mater, a tough, fibrous membrane that turns inward to form a meningeal layer that envelops the brain (Plate 81). The vertebral cav-ty houses the spinal cord, its coverings, related vessels, and nerve roots (Plate 77). Its dura mater is continuous with the cranial dura at the foramen magnum, and it forms a sac whose bottom is at the level of the 2nd sacral vertebra.

The thoracic cavity contains the lungs, heart, and other structures (tubular airways, blood vessels, lymphatics, nerves) in the chest. Its skeletal walls are the thoracic vertebrae and ribs posteriorly, the ribs anterolaterally, and the sternum and costal cartilages anteriorly (Plate 80). The roof of the cavity is membranous; the floor is the muscular thoracic diaphragm (Plate 50). The middle of the thoracic cavity has a partition filled with structure (e.g., heart), called the mediastinum (Plate 104). It separates the thoracic cavity into discrete left and right parts (not shown).The internal surface of each half of the thoracic cavity is completely lined with a serous membrane called pleura (Plate 133). The pleura, like all serous membranes, consists of a single layer of cells supported by a thin, vascular, connective tissue layer. These cells secrete a serous fluid that permits the pleura-lined lungs to move against the pleura-lined thoracic walls without friction.

The abdominal cavity, containing the gastrointestinal tract and related glands, the urinary tract, and great numbers of vessels and nerves, has muscular walls anterolaterally, the lower ribs and muscle laterally, and the lumbar vertebrae posteriorly. The roof of the abdominal cavity is the thoracic diaphragm. The abdominal and pelvic cavities are continuous with one another and share the muscular pelvic floor. The pelvic cavity, containing the urinary bladder, rectum, and reproductive organs, has muscular walls anteriorly, bony walls laterally, and the sacrum posteri-orly. The internal surface of the abdominal wall is lined by a serous membrane, the peritoneum (Plate 140).The serous secretions enable the mobile abdominal viscera to slip and slide frictionlessly during movement. The peritoneum drapes over the pelvic viscera, does not envelop them, and does not reach the pelvic floor.

OPEN VISCERAL CAVITIES

RESPIRATORY TRACT E
URINARY TRACT F
DIGESTIVE TRACT G
MUCOSA H

Open cavities (*respiratory, digestive, urinary* tracts) are largely tubular passageways lined with a mucus-secreting layer called a *mucosa*. The mucosa is the working tissue (secretion, absorption, protection) of open cavities; it is lined with epithelial cells, is supported by vascular con-nective tissue, and often incorporates a smooth muscle layer. Open cavities within the thoracic and abdominopelvic cavities are open to the outside of the body. Their mucosal lining is continuous with the skin at the ends of the tubular cavities (nose, mouth, perineum).

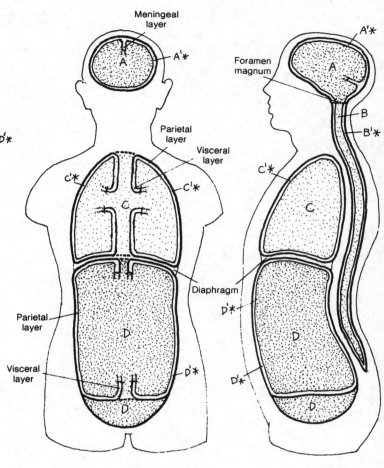

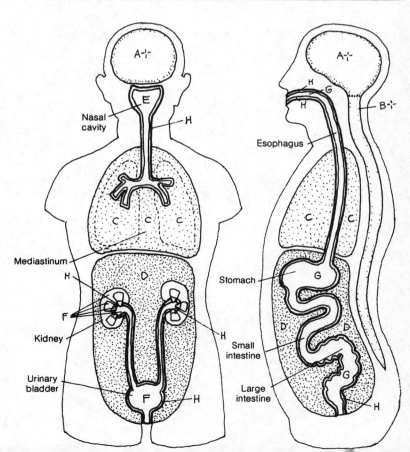

THE GENERALIZED CELL

CN: Color gray the variety of cell shapes at upper left. Use lightest colors for A, C, D, F and G. (1) Small circles representing ribosomes (H) are found throughout the cytoplasm (F) and on the rough endoplasmic reticulum (G¹); color those larger areas, including the ribosomes, first, and then color over the ribosomes again with a darker color. Each organelle shown is just one of many found in the living cell.

CELL SHAPES *

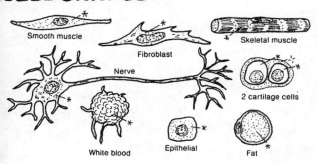

Smooth muscle

Fibroblast

Skeletal muscle

Nerve

2 cartilage cells

White blood

Epithelial

Fat

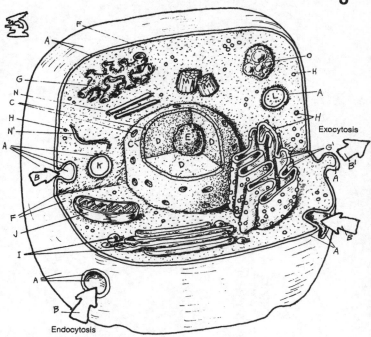

Exocytosis

Endocytosis

ORGANELLES :-

CELL MEMBRANE A
   ENDOCYTOSIS B / EXOCYTOSIS B'
NUCLEAR MEMBRANE C
NUCLEOPLASM D
NUCLEOLUS E
CYTOPLASM F
ENDOPLASMIC RETICULUM
   SMOOTH, G ROUGH G'
RIBOSOME H
GOLGI COMPLEX I
MITOCHONDRION J
VACUOLE K
LYSOSOME L
CENTRIOLE M
MICROTUBULE N
MICROFILAMENT N'
CELL INCLUSION O

The cell is the basic structural and functional unit of all living things. Living things are characterized by the ability to reproduce and grow, metabolize (transform or produce/consume of energy), and adapt to limited changes in their internal and external environment. Body structure lacking these characteristics, such as connective tissue fibers, is not considered to be "alive." Body structure more complex than a cell consists of a collection of cells and their products.

The activities of cells constitute the life process; they include ingestion, assimilation, and digestion of nutrients and excretion of the residue; respiration; synthesis and degradation of materials; movement; and excitability or response to stimuli. The impairment or cessation of these activities in normal cells, whether caused by trauma, infection, tumors, degeneration, or congenital defects, is the basis of a disordered or disease process.

By volume, the generalized cell is 80% water; by weight, it is composed of proteins (about 15%), lipids (3%), carbohydrates (1%), and nucleic acids and minerals (1%). These materials may be integrated into structural working units (organelles), form a more mobile functional unit (e.g., messenger RNA, globular protein-based enzymes), or form products of the cell. The basic function of a cell is to produce protein, which is essential to the acquisition and use of cell energy, formation and repair of structure, and cell activities (e.g., synthesis, secretion, absorption, contraction).

Cell membrane: the limiting lipoprotein membrane of the cell; retains internal structure; permits exportation and importation of materials. Infolding/outfolding of the cell membrane permits the introduction of material into the cell (endocytosis) or its expulsion (exocytosis) from the cell.

Nuclear membrane: porous, limiting, lipoprotein membrane; regulates passage of molecules.

Nucleoplasm: the nuclear substance containing chromatin (chromosomes during cell division) and RNA.

Nucleolus: a mass of largely RNA, it forms ribosobal RNA (RNAr) that passes into cytoplasm and becomes the site of protein synthesis.

Cytoplasm: the ground substance of the cell less the nucleus. Contains organelles and inclusions listed below.

Smooth/rough endoplasmic reticulum (ER): membrane-lined tubules to which ribosomes may be attached (rough ER; flattened tubules) or not (smooth ER; rounded tubules). Rough ER is concerned with transport of protein synthesized at the ribosomes. Smooth ER synthesizes complex molecules called steroids in some cells; stores calcium ions in muscle; breaks down toxins in liver.

Ribosome: the site of protein synthesis where amino acids are strung in sequence as directed by messenger RNA from the nucleus.

Golgi complex: flattened membrane-lined sacs that bud off small vesicles from the edges; collect secretory products and package them for export or cell use, e.g., lysomes.

Mitochondrion: membranous, oblong structure in which the inner membrane is convoluted like a maze. Energy for cell operations is generated here through a complex series of reactions between oxygen and products of digestion (oxidative reactions).

Vacuoles: membrane-lined containers that can merge with one another or other membrane-lined structure, such as the cell membrane. They function as transport vehicles.

Lysosome: membrane-lined container of enzymes with great capacity to break down structure, e.g., microorganisms, damaged cell parts, and ingested nutrients.

Centriole: bundle of microtubules in the shape of a short barrel; usually seen paired, perpendicular to one another. They give rise to spindles used by migrating chromatids during cell division.

Microtubules: formed of protein; provide structural support for the cell and/or its parts.

Microfilaments: are support structures formed of protein different from that of microtubules. In skeletal muscle, the proteins actin and myosin are examples of thin and thick microfilaments.

Cell inclusion: aggregation of material within the cell that is not a functional part (organelle) of the cell—e.g., glycogen, lipid.

CELL DIVISON / MITOSIS

CN: Use the colors you used on Plate 8 for cell membrane, nuclear membrane, nucleolus, and centriole for those titles on this plate, even though the previous letter labels may be different. Use contrasting colors for E–E² and F–F², and gray for D–D¹ to distinguish the latter from those with the contrasting colors. (1) Begin with the cell in interphase, reading the related text and completing each cell before going on to the next. (2) Color the name of each stage and its appropriate arrow of progression. Note that in interphase, the chromatin material within the nuclear membrane is in a thread-like state; color over the entire area with the appropriate color. Note that the starting chromatin (D* in interphase) is colored differently in the daughter cells (E², F²); it is the same chromatin.

CELL MEMBRANE A
NUCLEAR MEMBRANE B
NUCLEOLUS C
CHROMATIN D*/CHROMOSOME D¹*
CHROMATID E /CHROMOSOME E¹
   CHROMATIN E²
CHROMATID F /CHROMOSOME F¹
   CHROMATIN F²
CENTROMERE G
CENTRIOLE H
ASTER I
SPINDLE J

The ability to reproduce their kind is a characteristic of living things. Cells reproduce in a process of duplication and division called mitosis. Epithelial and connective cells reproduce frequently, mature muscle cells not so frequently, and mature nerve cells rarely if at all. Overactive mitosis may result in the formation of an encapsulated tumor; uncontrolled mitosis, associated with invasiveness and metastases, is called cancer.

As the main cellular changes during mitosis occur in the nucleus and surrounding area, only these parts of the cell are illustrated here. We show here how the nuclear chromatin (diffuse network of DNA and related protein), once duplicated, transforms into 46 chromosomes, which divide into paired subunits (92 chromatids); those chromatids separate and move into opposite ends of the dividing cell, forming the 46 chromosomes of each of the newly formed daughter cells. For clarity, we show only four pairs of chromatids and chromosomes. The phases of the observed nuclear changes during mitosis are as follows.

Interphase: the longest period of the reproductive cycle; the phase between successive divisions. Duplication of DNA (in chromatin) occurs during this phase. The dispersed chromatin (D*) here is a network of fine fibrils, not visible as discrete entities in the nucleoplasm. The cell membrane, nucleus, and nucleolus are intact. The centrioles are paired and adjacent to one another at one pole of the cell.

Prophase: the dispersed chromatin (D*) thickens, shortens, and coils to form condensed chromatin or chromosomes (D¹*). Each chromosome consists of two chromatids (E and F) connected by a centromere (G). Each chromatid has the equivalent amount of DNA of a chromosome. In the latter part of this phase, the nuclear membrane breaks up and dissolves, as does the nucleolus. The centrioles, having duplicated during interphase, separate, going to opposite poles of the cell. They project microtubules called asters.

Metaphase: strands of spindle fibers project across the cell center from paired centrioles. The chromatids attach to the spindle fibers at the centromere and line up in the center, half (46) on one side, half on the other.

Anaphase: the centromeres divide, each daughter centromere attached to one chromatid. Each centromere is drawn to the ipsilateral pole of the cell, along the track of the spindle fiber, taking its chromatid with it. The separated chromatids now constitute chromosomes. Anaphase ends when the daughter chromosomes arrive at their respective poles (46 on each side).

Telophase: the cell pinches off in the center, forming two daughter cells, each identical to the mother cell (assuming no mutations). The cytoplasm and organelles had duplicated earlier and are segregated into their respective newly-forming cells. As the nucleus is reconstituted, and the nuclear membrane and nucleolus reappear in each new cell, the chromosomes fade into dispersed chromatin, and the centromere disappears. Complete cleavage of the parent cell into daughter cells terminates the mitotic process. Each daughter cell enters interphase to start the process anew. The process of cell division increases cell numbers, and does not change cellular content.

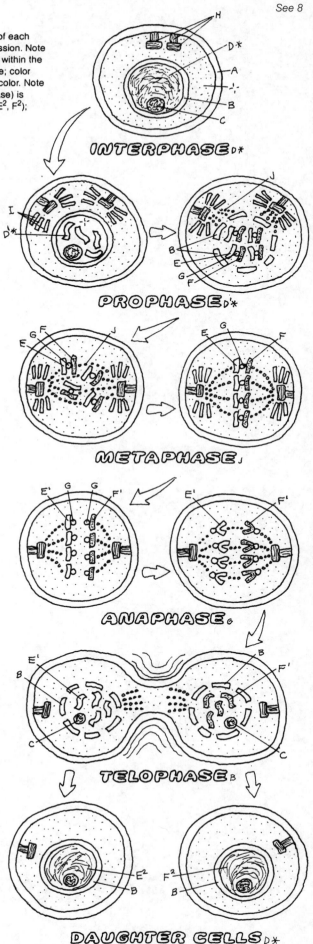

INTERPHASE D*

PROPHASE D¹*

METAPHASE J

ANAPHASE G

TELOPHASE B

DAUGHTER CELLS D*

TISSUES: EPITHELIUM

CN: Use very light colors throughout. (1) Color the arrows pointing to the location of the epithelial tissues in the body organs.

Epithelial tissues, one of four basic tissue types, form the working surface of skin and all body cavities, including glands, ducts, and vessels. They protect, secrete, absorb, or sense (e.g., neuroepithelia). Some even contract (myoepithelia). Epithelial tissues generally exist as one layer (simple) or more (stratified). The lowest layer of epithelia is bound to the underlying connective tissue by a basement membrane (secreted basal and reticular laminae). Epithelial cells are connected together by one or more of: adhesive glycoproteins, desmosomes, gap junctions, and circumferential bands (not shown).

SIMPLE EPITHELIUM

This surface tissue functions in filtration, diffusion, secretion, and absorption.

SQUAMOUS ᴀ

Simple squamous epithelia are thin, plate-like cells. They function in diffusion. They line the heart and all blood vessels (endothelia), air cells, body cavities (mesothelia), etc.

CUBOIDAL ʙ

Simple cuboidal epithelia are generally secretory cells and make up glands throughout the body, tubules of the kidney, terminal bronchioles of the lungs, and ducts of the reproductive tracts.

COLUMNAR ᴄ

Simple columnar epithelia line the gastrointestinal tract and are concerned with secretion and absorption. Their free (apical) surface may be covered with finger-like projections of cell membrane called microvilli, increasing the cell's surface area for secretion/absorption.

PSEUDOSTRATIFIED COLUMNAR ᴅ

Columnar cells bunched together form a single layer, appearing as if stratified. Each cell is attached to the basement membrane. These cells line reproductive and respiratory tracts. Cilia on the free surface collectively move surface material by means of undulating power strokes alternating with resting strokes.

STRATIFIED EPITHELIUM

Stratified epithelia are generally resistant to damage by wear and tear because of ready replacement of cells.

STRATIFIED SQUAMOUS ᴇ

This tissue may be keratinized (skin) or not (oral cavity, pharynx, vocal folds, esophagus, vagina, anus). Basal cells are generally columnar and germinating.

TRANSITIONAL ꜰ

Multiple layers of cells line the urinary tract. In the empty bladder, the fibromuscular layer is contracted because of muscle tone; the epithelia are closely concentrated. With bladder distension, cells are stretched out; the tissue is thinner than in the contracted state. The tissue is responsive to volume changes.

GLANDULAR EPITHELIUM

Glandular cells produce and secrete/excrete materials of varying composition—e.g., sweat, milk, sebum, cerumen, hormones, enzymes. Myoepithelial cells induce discharge of the secreted material in most cases.

EXOCRINE ɢ

Exocrine glands (e.g., sweat, sebaceous, pancreatic, mammary) arise as outpocketings of epithelial lining tissue, retain a duct to the free surface of the cavity or skin, and excrete/secrete some substance. Secretory portions may have one of several shapes (tubular, coiled, alveolar/acinar) connected to one or more ducts.

ENDOCRINE ʜ

Endocrine glands arise as epithelial outgrowths but lose their connections to the surface during development. They are intimately associated with a dense capillary network and secrete their products into it.

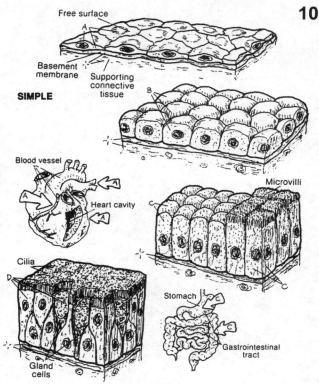

SIMPLE

Free surface · Basement membrane · Supporting connective tissue · Blood vessel · Heart cavity · Microvilli · Cilia · Stomach · Gastrointestinal tract · Gland cells

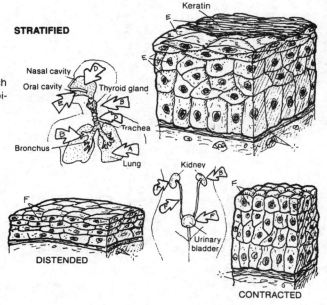

STRATIFIED

Keratin · Nasal cavity · Oral cavity · Thyroid gland · Trachea · Bronchus · Lung · Kidney · Urinary bladder · DISTENDED · CONTRACTED

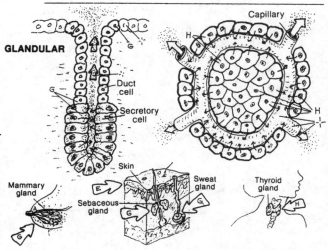

GLANDULAR

Capillary · Duct cell · Secretory cell · Mammary gland · Sebaceous gland · Sweat gland · Skin · Thyroid gland

TISSUES: FIBROUS CONNECTIVE TISSUES

CN: Use yellow for C and C^1, and red for J. (1) Begin with the illustration at middle left and the related titles (A through K). The titles and borders of the microscopic sections of dense regular/irregular c.t. (F^1, F^2) receive the color of collagen (F), as that is the dominant structure in both tissues. (2) Do not color the matrix.

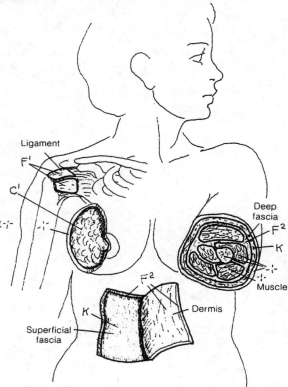

CELLS
FIBROBLASTₐ
MACROPHAGEᵦ
FAT CELLc
PLASMA CELLᴅ
MAST CELLᴇ

FIBERS
COLLAGENF
ELASTICɢ
RETICULARʜ

MATRIX, GROUND SUBSTANCE
CAPILLARYⱼ

Illustration labels: Ligament, F¹, C¹, F², Deep fascia, K, Muscle, Dermis, Superficial fascia, K

The connective tissues (c.t.) connect, bind, and support body structure. They consist of variable numbers of cells, fibers, and ground substance (fluid, viscous sol/gel, or mineralized). At the microscopic level (here illustrated at about 600× magnification), connective tissues range from blood (cells/fluid), through the fibrous tissues (cells/fibers/variable matrix) to the more stiff supporting tissues (cells/fibers/dense matrix) of cartilage and mineralized bone. Connective tissue can be seen at visible levels of body organization as well, in fascial layers of the body wall, tendons, ligaments, bone, and so on. This plate introduces the fibrous connective tissues (c.t. proper).

LOOSE, AREOLAR C.T. K

Loose, areolar connective tissue is characterized by many cells, a loose, irregular arrangement of fibers, and a moderately viscous fluid matrix. *Fibroblasts* secrete the fibers and ground substance of this tissue. Mobile *macrophages* engulf cell debris, foreign matter, and microorganisms. *Fat cells*, storing lipids, may be seen in small numbers or large (adipose tissue). *Plasma cells* secrete antibodies in response to infection. *Mast cells* contain heparin and other secretory products, some of which initiate allergic reactions when released. Numerous other cells may transit the loose fibrous tissues, including white blood cells (leukocytes). *Collagen* (linkages of protein exhibiting great tensile strength) and *elastic fibers* (made of the protein elastin) are the fibrous support elements in this tissue. *Reticular tissue* is a smaller form of collagen, forming supporting networks around cell groups of the blood-forming tissues, the lymphoid tissues, and adipose tissue. The *matrix* (consisting largely of water with glycoproteins and glycosaminoglycans in solution) is the intercellular ground substance in which all of the above function; it is fluid-like in the fibrous tissue. Numerous *capillaries* roam throughout this tissue. Loose connective tissue found deep to the skin is called superficial fascia, subcutaneous tissue, or hypodermis. It is found deep to the epithelial tissues of mucous and serous membranes of hollow organs.

ADIPOSE C.T. c'

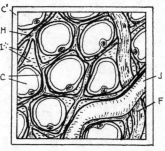

Adipose tissue is an aggregation of *fat cells*, supported by reticular and collagenous fibers and closely associated with both blood and lymph capillaries. The storage/release of fat in/from adipose tissue is regulated by hormones (including nutritional factors) and nervous stimuli. It serves as a source of fuel, an insulator, and mechanical padding and stores fat-soluble vitamins. Adipose tissue is located primarily in the superficial fasciae (largely breast, buttock, anterior abdominal wall, arm, and thigh), yellow marrow, and the surface of serous membranes.

DENSE REGULAR C.T. F¹

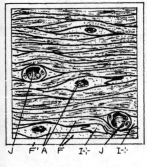

Dense, parallel-arranged, masses of collagenous/elastic fibers form ligaments and tendons that are powerfully resistant to axially loaded tension forces, yet permit some stretch. Tendons/ligaments contain few cells, largely fibroblasts. Elastic, dense regular ligaments are found in the posterior neck and between vertebrae; the tendocalcaneus is the largest elastic structure (tendon or ligament) in the body, storing energy used in gait.

DENSE IRREGULAR C.T. F²

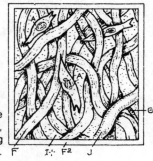

Dense, irregularly arranged masses of interwoven collagenous (and some elastic) fibers in a viscous matrix form capsules of joints, envelop muscle tissue (deep fasciae), encapsulate certain visceral organs (liver, spleen, and others), and largely make up the dermis of the skin. The tissue is impact resistant (bearing stress omnidirectionally), contains few cells, and is minimally vascularized.

TISSUES: SUPPORTING CONNECTIVE TISSUES

CN: Use the same colors as used on the previous plate for collagen (D) and elastic (E) fibers. Use a light tan or yellow for F and red for L. Use light colors for A, B, G, I, and M. Complete the upper material before coloring the bone section.

CARTILAGE
CHONDROCYTE A
LACUNA B
MATRIX C
COLLAGEN FIBER D
ELASTIC FIBER E

Microscopic sections of cartilage tissue reveal cells (chondrocytes) in small cavities (lacunae) surrounded by a hard but flexible matrix of water bound to proteoglycans and collagen fibers. Avascular cartilage receives its nutrition by diffusion from vessels in the perichondrium. For that reason, cartilage does not repair well after injury, yet it is often a part of a temporary framework (callus) in the healing process of fractured bone. There are three types of cartilage.

Bone is unique for its mineralized matrix (65% mineral, 35% organic by weight). The skeleton is bone. Bone is a reservoir of calcium; it is an anchor for muscles, tendons, and ligaments; it harbors many viscera; it assists in the mechanism of respiration; its cavity in certain bones is a center of blood-forming activity (hematopoiesis); in other bones, its cavity is a storage site for lipid.

FIBROCARTILAGE D'

Fibrocartilage offers strength with flexibility, resisting both impact and tensile forces. The best example of this tissue is the intervertebral disc. It consists of dense fibrous tissue interspersed with cartilage cells and a relatively small amount of intercellular matrix.

ELASTIC CARTILAGE E'

This tissue is essentially hyaline cartilage with elastic fibers and some collagen. It supports the external ear and the epiglottis of the larynx. Feel its unique flexibility in your own external ear.

HYALINE CARTILAGE A'

Well known as the covering at bone ends (articular cartilage), hyaline cartilage is avascular, insensitive, and compressible. It is porous, enhancing absorption of nutrients and oxygen. It supports the external nose (feel and compare with the elastic cartilage of the ear). It is the main structural support of the larynx and much of the lower respiratory tract. It forms the model for most early developing bone (Plate 168).

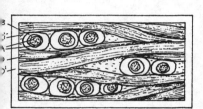
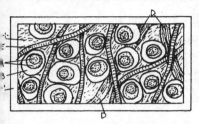

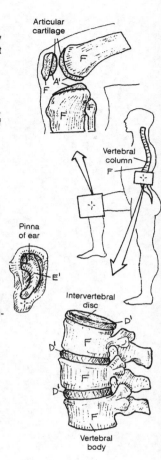

BONE F
PERIOSTEUM F'
COMPACT BONE G
HAVERSIAN SYS. *
HAV. CANAL H
LAMELLAE G'
OSTEOCYTE I
OSTEOCLAST I'
LACUNA B
CANALICULI J
VOLKMANN CANAL K
BLOOD VESSEL L
SPONGY BONE G²

As you read, check Plate 20. Bone has compact and cancellous forms. Compact bone is the impact-resistant, weight-bearing shell of bone lined by a sheath of life-supporting fibrous periosteum. Compact bone consists of columns called haversian systems or osteons: concentric layers (lamellae) of mineralized, collagenous matrix around a central (haversian) canal containing blood vessels. Volkmann's canals interconnect the haversian canals. Note the interstitial lamellae between columns and the circumferential lamellae enclosing the columns. Between lamellae are small cavities (lacunae) interconnected by little canals (canaliculi). Bone cells (osteocytes) and their multiple extensions fill these spaces, which connect with the haversian canal. In areas of resorbing bone matrix, large, multinucleated, avidly phagocytic osteoclasts can be seen with multiple cytoplasmic projections facing the matrix they are destroying. Bone-forming cells (osteoblasts) can be seen in Plate 168. Cancellous bone is internal to compact bone and is especially well seen at the ends of long bones. It consists of irregularly-shaped, interwoven beams (trabeculae) of bone, lacking haversian systems.

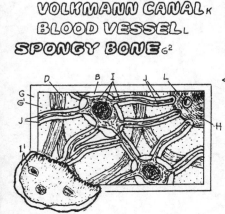

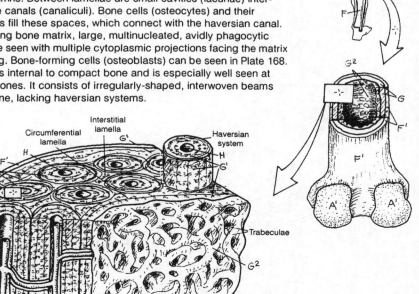

TISSUES: MUSCLE

Muscle tissue, one of the four basic tissue types of the body, consists of muscle cells ("fibers") and their fibrous connective tissue coverings. There are three kinds of muscle tissues: skeletal, cardiac, and smooth. Muscle tissue shortens (contracts) in response to nerve, nerve-like, or hormonal stimulation. Depending on their attachments, skeletal muscles move bones at joints, constrict cavities, and move the skin; cardiac muscle compresses a heart cavity or orchestrates the sequence of cardiac muscle contraction; and smooth muscle moves the contents of cavities by rhythmic contractions, constricts vessels it surrounds, and moves hairs/closes pores of the skin. The surrounding *connective tissue* transfers the force of contraction from cell to cell and supports the muscle fibers and the many blood *capillaries* and nerves that supply them.

SKELETAL/STRIATED MUSCLE, E
SARCOLEMMA F   CELL E'

Skeletal muscle cells are long, striated, and *multinucleated*, formed of myofibrils, *mitochondria*, and other organelles within the cytoplasm (sarcoplasm). Each cell is enveloped in a cell membrane called *sarcolemma*. Collections of muscle cells make up the belly of a muscle. The highly vascularized skeletal muscles contribute greatly to the size and shape of the body. Skeletal muscles attach to bones or other muscles at their tendinous ends. Between bony attachments, muscles cross one or more joints, moving them. Muscles always pull; they never push. Skeletal muscle contractions consist of rapid, brief shortenings, often generating considerable force. Each contracting cell shortens maximally. Three kinds of skeletal muscle fibers are recognized: red (small, dark, long-acting, slow-contracting, postural muscle fibers with oxygen-rich myoglobin and many mitochondria), white (relatively large, pale, anaerobic, short-acting, fast-contracting muscle fibers with few mitochondria), and intermediate fibers. With exercise, fast fibers can convert to slow; slow fibers can convert to fast. Contraction of skeletal muscle requires nerves (innervation). Without a nerve supply (denervation), skeletal muscle cells cease to shorten; without reinnervation, the cells will die. A denervated portion of muscle loses its tone and becomes flaccid. In time, the entire muscle will become smaller (atrophy). Muscle contraction is generally under voluntary control, but the brain involuntarily maintains a degree of contraction among the body's skeletal muscles (muscle tone). After injury, skeletal muscle cells can regenerate from myoblasts with moderate functional significance; such regeneration may also occur in association with muscle cell hypertrophy in response to training/exercise.

CARDIAC/STRIATED MUSCLE, G
INTERCALATED DISC H   CELL G'

Cardiac muscle cells make up the heart muscle. They are branched, striated cells with one or two centrally located nuclei and a sarcolemma surrounding the sarcoplasm. They are connected to one another by junctional complexes called *intercalated discs*. Their structure is similar to skeletal muscle, but less organized. Cardiac muscle is highly vascularized; its contractions are rhythmic, strong, and well regulated by a special set of impulse-conducting muscle cells, not nerves. Rates of contraction of cardiac muscle are mediated by the autonomic (visceral) nervous system, the nerves of which increase/decrease heart rate. Cardiac muscle is probably not capable of regeneration.

VISCERAL/SMOOTH MUSCLE, I
PLASMALEMMA F'   CELL I'

Smooth muscle cells are long, tapered cells with centrally placed nuclei. Each cell is surrounded by a *plasmalemma* (cell membrane). These cells are smooth (nonstriated). Myofibrils are not seen; the myofilaments intersect with one another in a pattern less organized than that seen in skeletal muscle. Smooth muscle cells occupy the walls of organs with cavities (viscera) and serve to propel the contents along the length of those cavities by slow, sustained, often powerful rhythmic contractions (consider menstrual or intestinal cramps). Smooth muscle cells, oriented perpendicular to the flow of tubular contents, act as gates (sphincters) in specific sites, regulating the flow, as in delaying the flow of urine. Well-vascularized, smooth muscle fibers contract in response to both autonomic nerves and hormones. They are also capable of spontaneous contraction. Regeneration of smooth muscle, to some extent, is possible after injury.

CN: Use red for C and your lightest colors for B, E, G, and I. (1) The sarcolemma (F), which covers each skeletal and cardiac muscle cell, is colored only at the cut ends. The plasmalemma (F¹), which covers each smooth muscle cell, is colored only at the cut ends. (2) The nuclei of cardiac and smooth muscle cells, located deep within the cells, are to be colored only at the cut ends (A). (3) One of the intercalated discs (H) of the cardiac cells has been separated to reveal its structure (schematically). (4) The cellular views are microscopic.

NUCLEUS A
CONNECTIVE TISSUE B
CAPILLARY C
MITOCHONDRION D

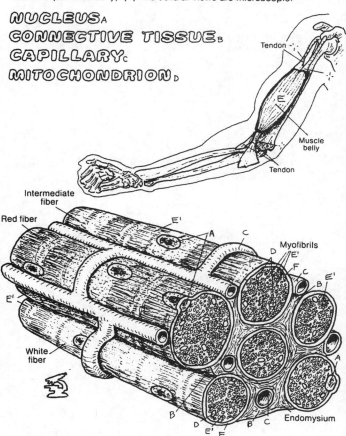

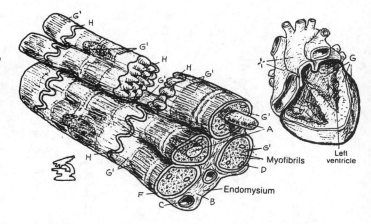

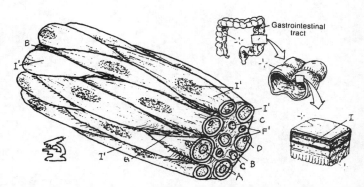

TISSUES: SKELETAL MUSCLE MICROSTRUCTURE

CN: Use the same colors used on Plate 13 for sarcolemma (A) and mitochondrion (D). Use the same color used on the skeletal muscle cell for the myofibril (E) here. Use light colors for G and J, a dark color for H, and very dark colors for F and K. The cell nucleus is not shown here. (1) Begin with the drawing of the arm. (2) Color the parts of the muscle cell in the central illustration; note the presence of mitochondria (D) between the myofibrils. (3) Color the parts of the exposed (lowest) myofibril and the color-related letters, bands, lines, zone. Note that the cut end of this myofibril receives the color E, for identification purposes, and is part of the A band of the sarcomere adjacent to the one to be colored. (4) Color the relaxed and contracted sarcomere, the filaments, and the mechanism for contraction, noting the color relationship with the myofibril and its parts.

A part of a skeletal muscle cell is shown with the *sarcolemma* opened to reveal some cellular contents. The most visible of the contents are the *myofibrils*, the contractile units of the cell. They are enveloped by a flat tubular *sarcoplasmic reticulum* (SR) that, in part, regulates the distribution of calcium ions (Ca++) into the myofibrils. Inward tubular extensions of the sarcolemma, called the *transverse tubule system* (TTS), run transversely across the SR, at the level of the Z lines of the myofibrils. The TTS, containing stores of sodium ions (Na+) and calcium ions (Ca++), conducts electrochemical excitation to the myofibrils from the sarcolemma. *Mitochondria* provide energy for the cell work.

The myofibrils consist of myofilaments: *thick filaments* (largely myosin) with heads that project outward as *cross bridges*, and *thin filaments* (largely actin) composed of two interwoven strands. These two filament types are arranged into contractile units, each of which is called a *sarcomere*. Each myofibril consists of several radially arranged sarcomeres. At the end of each sarcomere, the thin filaments are permanently attached to the *Z line*, which separates one sarcomere from the next. The relative arrangement of the thick and thin filaments in the sarcomere creates light (*I, H*) and dark (*A*) *bands/zone* and the *M line*, all of which contribute to the appearance of cross-striations in skeletal (and cardiac) muscles.

Shortening of a myofibril occurs when the thin filaments slide toward the center (H zone), bringing the Z lines closer together in each sarcomere. The filaments do not shorten; the myosin filaments do not move. The close relationship of the TTS to the Z lines suggests that this site is the "trigger area" for induction of the sliding mechanism. This sliding motion is induced by *cross bridges* (heads of the immovable thick filaments) that are connected to the thin filaments. Activated by high-energy bonds from ATP, the paddle-like cross bridges swing in concert toward the H zone, drawing the thin filaments with them. The sarcomere shortens as the opposing thin filaments meet or even overlap at the M line.

Occurring simultaneously in all or most of the myofibrils of a muscle cell, shortening of sarcomeres translates to a variable shortening of the resting length of the muscle cell. Repeated in hundreds of thousands of conditioned muscle cells of a professional athlete, the resultant contractile force can pull a baseball bat through an arc sufficient to send a hardball a hundred meters or more through the air.

SKELETAL MUSCLE CELL

SARCOLEMMA_A

SARCOPLASMIC RETICULUM_B

TRANSVERSE TUBULE SYS._C

MITOCHONDRION_D

MYOFIBRIL_E

SARCOMERE_F

I BAND_G

THIN FILAMENT (ACTIN)_{G'}

Z LINE_{F'}

A BAND_H

THICK FILAMENT (MYOSIN)_{H'}

CROSS BRIDGE_I

H ZONE_J

M LINE_K

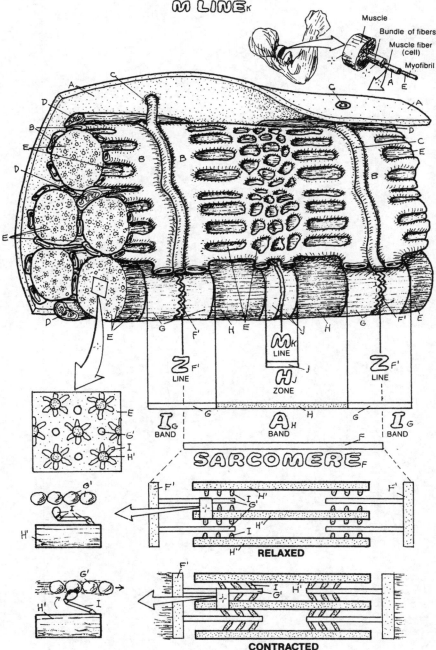

THIN FILAMENT_{G'}

THICK FILAMENT_{H'}

TISSUES: NERVOUS

CN: Use a light color for A. Note the small arrows that indicate direction of impulse conduction. The neurons of the peripheral nervous system shown at lower left are illustrated in the orientation of the left upper limb, although highly magnified.

NEURON:
CELL BODY A
PROCESS(ES):
DENDRITE B
AXON C

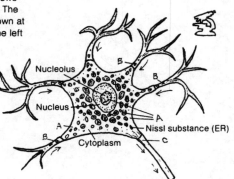

Nervous tissue consists of *neurons* (nerve cells) and *neuroglia*. Neurons generate and conduct electrochemical impulses by way of neuronal (cellular) *processes*. Neuroglia are the supporting, non-impulse-generating/conducting cells of the nervous system. The main, nucleus-bearing part of the neuron is the *cell body*. Its cytoplasm contains the usual cell organelles. Uniquely, the endoplasmic reticulum occurs in clusters called Nissl substance. Neurons do not undergo mitosis after birth, compromising their ability to regenerate after injury. Neuronal growth consists of migration and arborization of processes. Neurons are the impulse-conducting cells of the brain and spinal cord (central nervous system, or CNS) and the spinal and cranial nerves (peripheral nervous system, or PNS).

TYPES OF NEURONS:

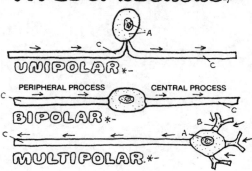

UNIPOLAR *
BIPOLAR *
MULTIPOLAR *

Neurons fall into three structural categories based on numbers of processes ("poles"). Processes that are highly branched (arborized) and uncovered are called *dendrites*. Slender, long, minimally branched processes are called *axons*. Within each category, there is a great variety of shape and size of neurons. *Unipolar* neurons have or appear to have (pseudounipolar) one process that splits near its cell body into a central and peripheral process. Both processes conduct impulses in the same direction, and each is termed an axon (see the sensory neuron at lower left). *Bipolar* neurons have two (central and peripheral) processes, called axons, conducting impulses in the same direction (see Plate 71). *Multipolar* neurons have three or more processes, one of which is an axon (see PNS motor neuron at lower left and CNS neuron at lower right).

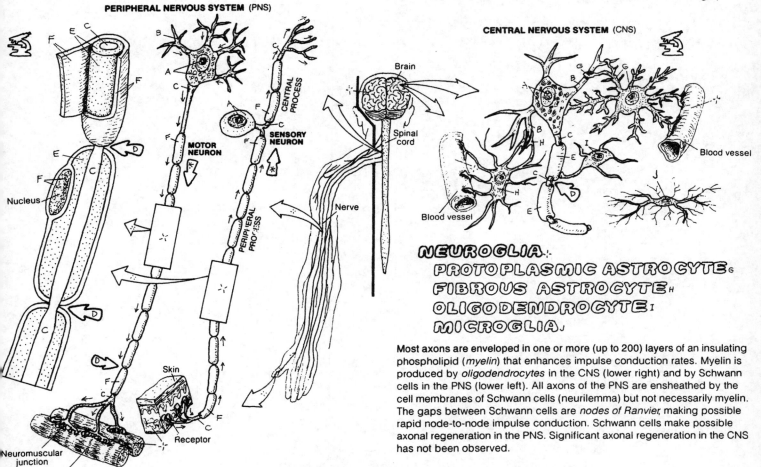

PERIPHERAL NERVOUS SYSTEM (PNS)

Nucleus

MOTOR NEURON

SENSORY NEURON

CENTRAL PROCESS

PERIPHERAL PROCESS

Brain

Spinal cord

Nerve

Skin

Receptor

Neuromuscular junction

Skeletal muscle

Blood vessel

CENTRAL NERVOUS SYSTEM (CNS)

Blood vessel

NEUROGLIA:
PROTOPLASMIC ASTROCYTE G
FIBROUS ASTROCYTE H
OLIGODENDROCYTE I
MICROGLIA J

Most axons are enveloped in one or more (up to 200) layers of an insulating phospholipid (*myelin*) that enhances impulse conduction rates. Myelin is produced by *oligodendrocytes* in the CNS (lower right) and by Schwann cells in the PNS (lower left). All axons of the PNS are ensheathed by the cell membranes of Schwann cells (neurilemma) but not necessarily myelin. The gaps between Schwann cells are *nodes of Ranvier*, making possible rapid node-to-node impulse conduction. Schwann cells make possible axonal regeneration in the PNS. Significant axonal regeneration in the CNS has not been observed.

NODE OF RANVIER D
AXON COVERINGS:
MYELIN E
SCHWANN CELL F

Neuroglia exist in both the CNS and PNS (Schwann cells). *Protoplasmic astrocytes* occur primarily in gray matter (dendrites, cell bodies) of the CNS, *fibrous astrocytes* in the white matter (myelinated axons). Their processes attach to both neurons and blood vessels and may offer metabolic, nutritional, and physical support. They may play a role in the blood/brain barrier. Oligodendrocytes are smaller than astrocytes, have fewer processes, and are seen near neurons. *Microglia* are the small scavenger cells of the brain and spinal cord.

NEUROMUSCULAR INTEGRATION

CN: Use very light colors for A and E, and a dark color for F.
(1) Begin with the skeletal muscle lifting the heel of the foot and complete the motor unit and the enlarged view of the neuromuscular junction. (2) Color carefully the motor units and related titles at the bottom of the plate: only the discharging motor units (in dark outline) are to be colored. Note that the word "partial" is not colored under the example of partial contraction.

SKELETAL MUSCLE A
MUSCLE FIBER A'
MOTOR END PLATE B
MOTOR NERVE C
AXON C'
AXON BRANCH D
AXON TERMINAL E

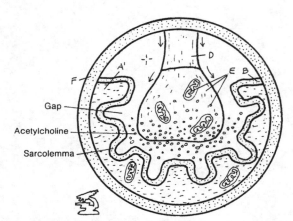

Gap

Acetylcholine

Sarcolemma

MOTOR UNIT
AXON C'
AXON BRANCH D
NEUROMUSCULAR JUNCTION F
MUSCLE FIBER A'

An axon of a single motor neuron, its axon branches, and the skeletal muscle fibers with which they form neuromuscular junctions constitute a *motor unit*. Within any given skeletal muscle, the number of muscle fibers innervated by a single motor neuron largely determines the specificity of contraction of that muscle; the fewer the number of muscle fibers in each motor unit, the more selective and refined the degree of contraction of that skeletal muscle.

NEUROMUSCULAR JUNCTION F
AXON TERMINAL E
MOTOR END PLATE B

Skeletal muscle consists of innumerable muscle fibers (cells). Skeletal muscle requires an intact nerve (innervation) to shorten (contract). Such a nerve, called a *motor nerve*, consists of numerous axons of motor neurons. A motor neuron (see Plate 15) is dedicated solely to stimulating muscle fibers to contract. Each single *muscle fiber* in a skeletal muscle is innervated by a *branch of an axon*. The microscopic site at which the axon branch attaches to the skeletal muscle fiber is called the *neuromuscular junction*. Each neuromuscular junction consists of an *axon terminal* closely applied to an area of convoluted muscle fiber sarcolemma called the *motor end plate*. There is a gap between the two surfaces. When a skeletal muscle fiber is about to be stimulated, a chemical neurotransmitter, called acetylcholine, is released by the axon terminal into the gap. The neurotransmitter induces a change in the permeability of the sarcolemma to sodium (Na^+), which initiates muscle fiber contraction. A muscle fiber can only contract maximally ("all or none" law).

GRADES OF CONTRACTION

Given the fact of "all or none" contraction by individual skeletal muscle fibers, grades of contraction of a skeletal muscle are made possible by activating a number of motor units and not activating others. A *resting muscle* activates no motor units. In a *partial contraction*, only some of the motor units are activated. In *maximal contraction* of a skeletal muscle, all motor units are activated. Gluteus maximus consists of skeletal muscle fibers having a nerve-to-muscle ratio of 1:1000 or more. There is no possibility of controlled, refined contractions from this muscle. The facial muscles, on the other hand, have a much lower nerve-to-muscle ratio, closer to 1:10. Here small numbers of muscle fibers can be contracted by implementing one or a few motor units, generating very fine control on the muscular effect (facial expression) desired.

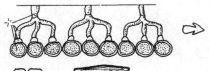

AT REST

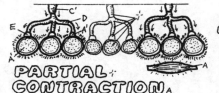

PARTIAL CONTRACTION A

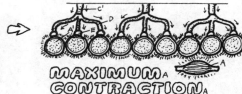

MAXIMUM CONTRACTION A

INTEGRATION OF TISSUES

This plate has one goal: to aid you in visually integrating the four basic tissues into somatic (body wall) and visceral (cavity-containing organs) structure. Concentrate on how the four tissues are arranged in each example of body structure. Consider the general function of each tissue in the overall function of the part/organ. There are an infinite number of functionally related variations in the way these four tissues form a discrete construction of the soma and viscera of the body.

CN: Use yellow for D and light, contrasting colors for A and B, and a medium brown for C. The various vessels that are shown in these tissues—arteries and veins above, and arterioles, venules, capillaries, and lymph vessels below—are not to be colored, as they are made up of more than one basic tissue. Note that within deep fascia, arteries are generally paired with veins.

SOMATIC STRUCTURE *-
EPITHELIAL TISSUE :-
SKIN (OUTER LAYER)A
CONNECTIVE TISSUE :-
SKIN (DEEP LAYER)B
SUPERFICIAL FASCIA B'
DEEP FASCIA B²
LIGAMENT B³
BONE B⁴
PERIOSTEUM B⁵
MUSCLE TISSUE :-
SKELETAL MUSCLE C
NERVOUS TISSUE :-
NERVE D

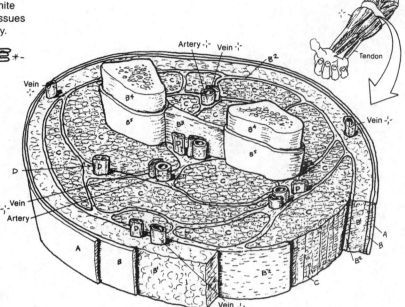

Somatic structure, making up the skin-covered musculoskeletal frame of the body, is concerned with stability, movement, and protection. Its construction reflects these functions. The outermost covering of the body wall everywhere is a protective keratinized *stratified squamous epithelial tissue*, constituting the *outer layer of skin* (epidermis). Other epithelial tissues in somatic structure are the inner layers of blood vessels, and the glands (not shown). Connective tissue layers of the body wall include the *deep layer of skin* (dermis), consisting of dense, irregular fibrous *connective tissue;* and the sub-adjacent, variously mobile, subcutaneous *superficial fascia* (loose connective and adipose tissues), containing cutaneous nerves, small vessels, and occasional large veins. *Deep fascia,* a more vascular, sensitive, dense, irregular fibrous tissue, ensheathes skeletal muscle (myofascial tissue) as well as the supporting nerves and vessels. *Ligaments* (dense regular connective tissue) bind *bone* to bone by way of *periosteum* (vascular, cellular, dense, irregular, fibrous tissue). Skeletal *muscles* and their *nerves* are packaged in groups, separated by slippery septa of deep fascia securing neurovascular structure. The fibrous investments of skeletal muscle converge to form tendons of the muscle.

VISCERAL STRUCTURE *-
EPITHELIAL TISSUE :-
MUCOSAL LINING A'
GLAND A²
SEROSA (OUTER LAYER)A³
CONNECTIVE TISSUE :-
LAMINA PROPIA B⁶
SUBMUCOSA B⁷
SEROSA (INNER LAYER)B⁸
MUSCLE TISSUE :-
SMOOTH MUSCLE C'
NERVOUS TISSUE :-
NERVE CELLS D'

Visceral structure is generally concerned with absorbing, secreting, trapping, and/or moving food, air, secretions, and/or waste in its cavities. *Epithelial tissue* is the innermost layer (*mucosal lining*) of the thin and pliable visceral wall. It faces the lumen (cavity of the viscus); it is often a single layer of cells (esophagus, urinary tract, and reproductive tract excepted) and deals with the contents of the visceral cavity. *Glands,* unicellular or larger in the mucosa or submucosa, are epithelial, as are the inner layers of blood and lymph vessels. The mucosa includes a sub-epithelial layer of loose fibrous tissue (*lamina propria*), supporting mobile cells, glands, vessels, and *nerves.* The deepest layer of the mucosa (when present) is a thin *smooth muscle* layer moving finger-like projections (villi) of the mucosal surface. Deep to the mucosa is a dense fibrous tissue (*submucosa*), replete with large vessels and small nerves/nerve cells (intramural ganglia) supplying the mucosa. Deeper yet, two or three layers of smooth muscle (tunica muscularis), innervated by local nerve cells, move the visceral wall in peristaltic contractions. The outermost layer of the gastrointestinal tract is the slippery serosa: an *outer* secretory simple squamous epithelial layer and an *inner* supporting layer of light fibrous tissue.

THE INTEGUMENT: EPIDERMIS

CN: Use very light colors except for E, G, and H. (1) To the right of these notes, color the entire epidermis gray. (2) Color the strata of the epidermis in the larger skin section. The thicker part of stratum corneum (A) reflects the nature of glabrous (hair-deficient) skin. The stratum lucidum (C) exists only in glabrous skin; it is too thin a layer to be shown in these views. (3) Color the strata and their constituent cells in the lower illustration, beginning with the bottom layer (F) and working upward in the direction of cell migration. (4) Color the section of the nail and its supporting elements.

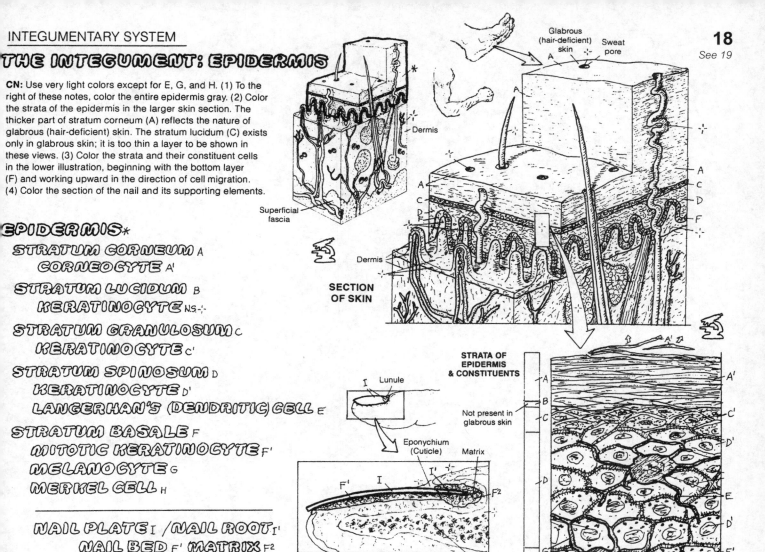

EPIDERMIS*

STRATUM CORNEUM A
    CORNEOCYTE A'
STRATUM LUCIDUM B
    KERATINOCYTE N.S.
STRATUM GRANULOSUM C
    KERATINOCYTE C'
STRATUM SPINOSUM D
    KERATINOCYTE D'
    LANGERHAN'S (DENDRITIC) CELL E
STRATUM BASALE F
    MITOTIC KERATINOCYTE F'
    MELANOCYTE G
    MERKEL CELL H

NAIL PLATE I / NAIL ROOT I'
NAIL BED F' MATRIX F²

"There is no magician's mantle to compare with the skin in its diverse roles of waterproof, overcoat, sunshade, suit of armor and refrigerator, sensitive to the touch of a feather, to temperature, and to pain, withstanding the wear and tear of three score years and ten, and executing its own running repairs."[1]

The skin is composed of an avascular, stratified squamous epithelial layer (*epidermis*) and a vascular fibrous layer (*dermis*). Within each layer, there is considerable variation. The epithelial layer consists of 4–5 levels of keratin-producing epithelial cells (keratinocytes). Absent capillaries, the layers of epithelia receive their nutrition by diffusion. The outer layers of the epidermis reflect the effects of dehydration.

Mitotic keratinocytes are columnar or cuboidal epithelia forming a single layer (*stratum basale*) separated from the dermis by a basement membrane (epidermal-dermal junction). These are the germinating cells; their progeny are pushed upward by succeeding generations. *Melanocytes* produce melanin granules that disperse along their cytoplasmic extensions (dendrites). These dendrites are woven among the cells of the strata basale and spinosum, and they disseminate melanin among the keratinocytes. Melanin protects the skin from ultraviolet (UV) radiation. Merkel cells are very sensitive to mechanical deformation (touch) of the surface of the skin. The connection with the sensory axon (nerve fiber) is probably similar to a synapse (see Plates 72, 91).

The stratum spinosum consists of several levels of cuboidal and squamous keratinocytes. The cells here have many intracellular filaments that converge on the cell membrane at desmosomes (recall Plate 10). Intercellular tonofibrils, radiating out from the cell surface, can be seen in tissue preparations where their appearance is enhanced by cellular dehydration during processing. This gives a "prickly" appearance to the cells of this stratum. Another kind of dendritic cell, the *Langerhans cell*, is seen in both strata basale and spinosum as well as the dermis. These dendritic cells are essentially phagocytic and present antigen to T lymphocytes (see Plate 124).

The stratum granulosum consists of flattened keratinocytes characterized by disintegrated nuclei and cytoplasmic keratohyalin and lamellar granules. The lipid-rich content of the lamellar granules fills the intercellular spaces, greatly contributing to the impermeability of the skin.

The thin stratum lucidum is seen only in glabrous (hair-deficient) thick skin. Its squamous keratinocytes are filled with filaments; the nuclei of these cells have largely disappeared.

The outermost stratum corneum is composed of multiple layers of squamous, lifeless, keratin-filled cells (*corneocytes*). Keratin is a scleroprotein, the polypeptides of which are intertwined with filaments within the cytoplasm. Loosening and detaching of the dead, outer layers of the stratum corneum is ongoing and involves breaking the intercellular junctional devices (desmosomes, filaments, amorphous lipid substance). The stratum corneum may be as thin as 5 layers (skin of the eyelid) and as thick as 50 layers (plantar surface of the foot).

Nails are plates of compacted, highly keratinized cells of the stratum corneum. Located on the dorsal aspect of each digit, they are translucent, revealing the vascular *nail bed* below. The nail bed consists of the strata basale and spinosum only. The proximal part of the nail plate (*nail root*) fits into a groove under the proximal nail fold. The epithelia around the root are the matrix or the source tissue for the nail plate, and they extend from the region of the nail root to the lunule (lighter, opaque area at the proximal part of the nail plates, seen best on the thumb). The nail plate is formed as the epithelia of the matrix grow distally. The nail plate is continually pushed distally by the keratinizing epithelia migrating from the matrix.

[1]Quote taken, with permission, from Lockhart, R.D., Hamilton, G.F., and Fyfe, F.W. ANATOMY THE HUMAN BODY. 2nd ed., Faber and Faber, Publishers, Ltd., London, 1965.

THE INTEGUMENT: DERMIS

DERMIS

PAPILLARY LAYER /LOOSE C.T. A
DERMAL PAPILLA A'
RETICULAR LAYER /DENSE C.T. B
HAIR SHAFT C **/FOLLICLE** C'
ARRECTOR PILI MUSCLE D
SEBACEOUS GLAND E
EPITHELIAL CELL E'
SECRETION F
BURST EPITH. CELL E²
SEBUM F+E²
SWEAT GLAND G
DUCT EPITHELIUM G'
GLAND EPITHELIUM G²
SWEAT H

ARTERY I **VEIN** J
LYMPHATIC VESSEL K
NERVE L **/RECEPTOR** L'

CN: Use red for I, blue for J, green for K, yellow for L, and light colors for the rest. (1) In the skin section, color the hair shafts (C) and sweat pores (G) in the otherwise uncolored epidermis. (2) Follow the text carefully as you color the enlarged views of the sebaceous (E) and sweat (G) glands.

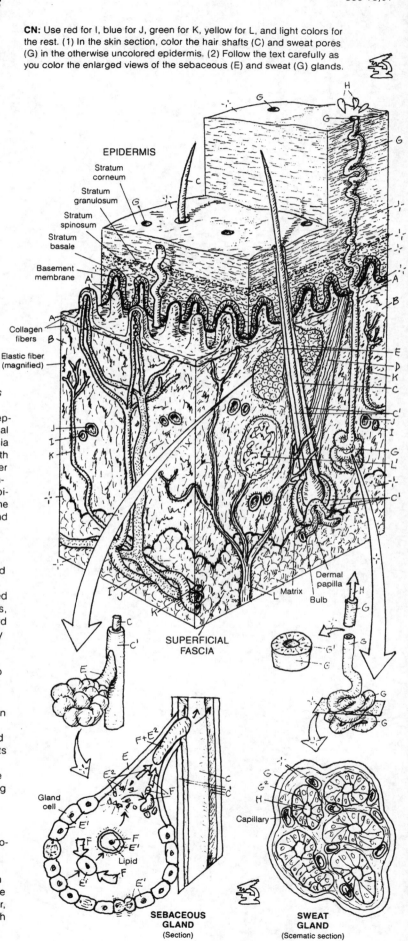

EPIDERMIS
Stratum corneum
Stratum granulosum
Stratum spinosum
Stratum basale
Basement membrane
Collagen fibers
Elastic fiber (magnified)
Dermal papilla
Matrix
Bulb
SUPERFICIAL FASCIA

Gland cell
Lipid
SEBACEOUS GLAND (Section)

Capillary
SWEAT GLAND (Scematic section)

The dermis consists of a fibrous connective tissue supporting *arteries* and *veins, lymphatic capillaries,* nerves and sensory receptors (see Plates 18, 91), and a number of accessory structures. The dermis is separated from the epidermis by a basement membrane (epidermal-dermal junction). On the deep side, the dermis is bordered by superficial fascia (hypodermis, subcutaneous tissue), a loose connective tissue layer with variable amounts of adipose tissue. The upper or most superficial layer of dermis is the *papillary layer*, characterized by a vascular, loose connective tissue. Pegs of this layer (dermal papillae) poke up into the epidermis. These pegs have strong attachment to the basement membrane and contain vessels, nerve endings, and axons among the collagen and elastic fibers. The subjacent *reticular layer* has a more dense fibrous character.

Hair shafts rise from epidermal *follicles* pushed down into the dermis (and hypodermis in the scalp) during development. They are not found in thick skin. The follicle begins at the site where the hair leaves the epidermis; it terminates in the form of a bulb. Hair shafts are composed of layers of keratin surrounded by layers of follicular cells (root sheaths, glassy membranes). The base of the follicle (hair bulb) is turned inward (invaginated) to accommodate a vascular dermal papilla. An obliquely placed bundle of smooth muscle attaches the outer membrane of the follicle to a papillary peg under the epidermis. This is the *arrector pili muscle*. When it is contracted, the hair to which it is attached erects to become perpendicular with the skin surface. In many mammals, hair standing on end is a sign of increased vigilance.

Sebaceous glands are grape-shaped collections of cells with a common duct (acini; holocrine gland) that surround hair follicles. The base of each gland is mitotically active; the daughter cells move into the gland center and become filled with lipid. Continued lipid engorgement results in *burst cells.* The secretory product and the cell debris constitute *sebum.* The gland duct transports the sebum to the epidermal surface or into the upper hair follicle. Sebum coats the skin and hairs, providing a degree of waterproofing. Sebum may play a social role, in terms of olfactory identification.

Sweat glands are coiled tubular glands in the deep dermis. The *ducts* of these glands traverse the epidermis by spiraling around the keratinocytes and open onto the epidermal surface. The glandular cells at the base of the sweat gland are in intimate proximity to capillaries, just as the glomerulus is in relation to the visceral layer of the renal capsule in the kidney. The cells produce sweat, a filtrate of plasma, somewhat like the filtrate of the renal corpuscle (Plate 149). Sweat is largely salt water, with a dash of urea and other molecules. Sweating is a means by which the hypothalamus can induce a degree of cooling by evaporation.

AXIAL/APPENDICULAR SKELETON

CN: Use light but contrasting colors for A and B.
(1) Color the axial skeleton (A) in all three views.
Do not color the spaces between the ribs (intercostal).
(2) Color the darker, outlined appendicular skeleton (B).
(3) Color the arrows identifying bone shape/classification.

CLASSIFICATION OF BONES:
LONG c
SHORT d
FLAT e
IRREGULAR f
SESAMOID g

Bones have a variety of shapes and defy classification by shape; yet such a classification historically exists. *Long bones* are clearly longer in one axis than in another; they are characterized by a medullary cavity, a hollow diaphysis of compact bone, and at least two epiphyses—e.g., femur, phalanx. *Short bones* are roughly cube-shaped; they are predominantly cancellous bone with a thin cortex of compact bone and have no cavity—e.g., carpal and tarsal bones. *Flat bones* (cranial bones, scapulae, ribs) are generally more flat than round, and *irregular bones* (vertebrae) have two or more different shapes. Bones not specifically long or short fit this latter category. *Sesamoid bones* are developed in tendons (e.g., patellar tendon); they are mostly bone, often mixed with fibrous tissue and cartilage. They have a cartilaginous articular surface facing an articular surface of an adjacent bone; they may be part of a synovial joint ensheathed within the fibrous joint capsule. The structures are generally pea-sized and are most commonly found in certain tendons/joint capsules in hands and feet, and occasionally in other articular sites of the upper and lower limbs. The largest is the patella, integrated in the tendon of quadriceps femoris. Sesamoid bones resist friction and compression, enhance joint movement, and may assist local circulation.

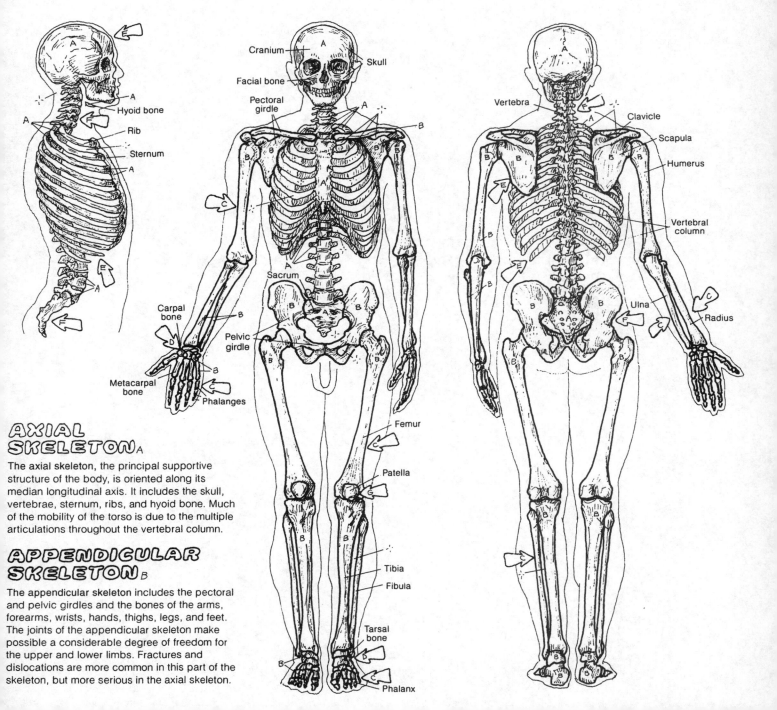

AXIAL SKELETON A

The axial skeleton, the principal supportive structure of the body, is oriented along its median longitudinal axis. It includes the skull, vertebrae, sternum, ribs, and hyoid bone. Much of the mobility of the torso is due to the multiple articulations throughout the vertebral column.

APPENDICULAR SKELETON B

The appendicular skeleton includes the pectoral and pelvic girdles and the bones of the arms, forearms, wrists, hands, thighs, legs, and feet. The joints of the appendicular skeleton make possible a considerable degree of freedom for the upper and lower limbs. Fractures and dislocations are more common in this part of the skeleton, but more serious in the axial skeleton.

CLASSIFICATION OF JOINTS

Bones are connected at joints (articulations). All bones move at joints. Joints are functionally classified as immovable (synarthroses), partly movable (amphiarthroses), or freely movable (diarthroses). The structural classification of joints is given below.

CN: Use a light blue for D, black for F, and gray for H.
(1) Do not color the bones in the upper half of the plate.
(2) Below, color the arrows pointing to the location of the joints as well as the joint representations.

FIBROUS JOINT:
IMMOVABLE_A / PARTLY MOVABLE_A'

Fibrous joints (synarthroses) are those in which the articulating bones are connected by fibrous tissue. Sutures of the skull are essentially *immovable fibrous joints*, especially after having ossified with age. Teeth in their sockets are fixed fibrous joints (gomphoses). Syndesmoses are *partly movable fibrous joints*, such as the interosseous ligaments between bones of the forearm or the bones of the leg.

CARTILAGINOUS JOINT:
IMMOVABLE_B / PARTLY MOVABLE_B'

Cartilaginous joints (synchondroses) are essentially immovable joints seen during growth—e.g., growth (epiphyseal) plates (see Plate 168). Fibrocartilaginous joints (amphiarthroses) are partly movable—e.g., the intervertebral disc. Symphyses also are partly movable fibrocartilagious joints, as between the pubic bones (symphysis pubis) and the manubrium and body of the sternum (sternal angle).

SYNOVIAL JOINT (FREELY MOVABLE):
ARTICULATING BONES_C:
ARTICULAR CARTILAGE_D
SYNOVIAL MEMBRANE_E
SYNOVIAL CAVITY (FLUID)_F•
JOINT CAPSULE_G
BURSA CAPSULE_G'
COLLATERAL LIGAMENT_H✷

Synovial joints (diarthroses) are freely movable within ligamentous limits and the bony architecture. They are characterized by *articulating bones* whose ends are capped with *articular cartilage* and are enclosed in a ligament-reinforced, sensitive, fibrous (joint) *capsule* lined internally with a vascular *synovial membrane* that secretes a lubricating fluid within the *cavity*. The synovial membrane does not cover articular cartilage. A fibrous tissue–lined synovial sac of fluid (bursa) often exists between moving structures outside the joint, as between tendon and bone. Bursae facilitate friction-free movement; friction may induce painful inflammation (bursitis).

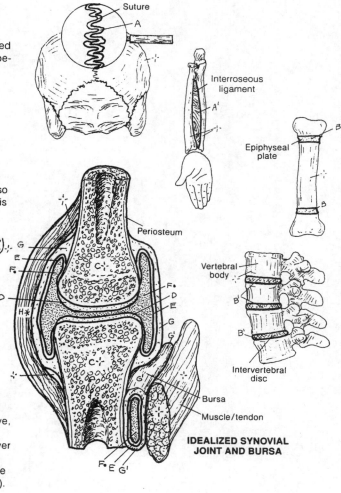

Suture

Interroseous ligament

Epiphyseal plate

Periosteum

Vertebral body

Intervertebral disc

Bursa

Muscle/tendon

IDEALIZED SYNOVIAL JOINT AND BURSA

TYPES OF SYNOVIAL JOINTS:

BALL & SOCKET_I

Ball-and-socket joints are best seen at the hip and shoulder. Movements in all direction are permitted—i.e., flexion, extension, adduction, abduction, internal and external rotation, and circumduction.

HINGE_J

A hinge joint permits movement in only one plane: flexion/extension. The ankle, interphalangeal, and elbow (humeroulnar) joints are hinge joints.

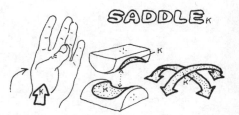

SADDLE_K

A saddle (sellar) joint—e.g., carpometacarpal joint at the base of the thumb—has two concave articulating surfaces, permitting all motions but rotation.

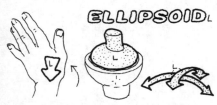

ELLIPSOID_L

The ellipsoid (condyloid, condylar) joint is a reduced ball-and-socket configuration in which significant rotation is largely excluded—e.g., the bicondylar knee, temporomandibular, and radiocarpal (wrist) joints.

PIVOT_M

A pivot joint has a ring of bone around a peg; e.g., the C1 vertebra rotates about the dens of C2, a rounded humeral capitulum on which the radial head pivots (rotates).

GLIDING_N

Gliding joints (e.g., the facet joints of the vertebrae, the acromio-clavicular, intercarpal, and intertarsal joints) has generally flat articulating surfaces.

TERMS OF MOVEMENTS

CN: Color the arrows pointing to the joints demonstrating the various movements of the body. Inversion (K) and eversion (L) movements occur among bones of the foot, not at the ankle.

EXTENSION_A
DORSIFLEXION_B
FLEXION_C
PLANTAR FLEXION_D
ADDUCTION_E
ABDUCTION_F
CIRCUMDUCTION_G
ROTATION_H
SUPINATION_I
PRONATION_J
INVERSION_K
EVERSION_L

Movements of bones occur at joints. Terms of movement are therefore applicable to joints, not bones (flexion of the humerus would break it!). Ranges of motion are limited by the bony architecture of a joint, related ligaments, and the muscles crossing that joint. It is from the anatomical position that specific directions of movement can be clearly delineated and ranges of motion measured.

Extension of a joint is to generally straighten it. In the anatomical position, most joints are in relaxed extension (neutral). In relation to the anatomical position, movements of extension are directed in the sagittal plane. Extreme, even abnormal extension is called hyperextension. At the ankle and wrist joints, extension is termed **dorsiflexion**.

Flexion of a joint is to bend it or decrease the angle between the bones of the joint. Movements of flexion are in the sagittal plane. At the ankle joint, flexion is also called **plantar flexion**.

Adduction of a joint moves a bone toward the midline of the body (or in the case of the fingers or toes, toward the midline of the hand or foot). In relation to the anatomical position, movements of adduction are directed in the coronal plane.

Abduction of a joint moves a bone away from the midline of the body (or hand or foot). Movements of abduction are directed in the coronal plane.

Circumduction is a circular movement, permitted at ball and socket, condylar, and saddle joints, characterized by flexion, abduction, extension, and adduction done in sequence.

Rotation of a joint is to turn the moving bone about its axis. Rotation toward the body is internal or medial rotation; rotation away from the body is external or lateral rotation.

Supination is external rotation of the radiohumeral joint. In the foot, supination involves lifting the medial aspect of the foot.

Pronation is internal rotation of the radiohumeral joint. In the foot, pronation involves raising the lateral aspect of the foot.

Inversion turns the sole of the foot inward so that the medial border of the foot is elevated.

Eversion turns the sole of the foot outward so that its lateral border is elevated.

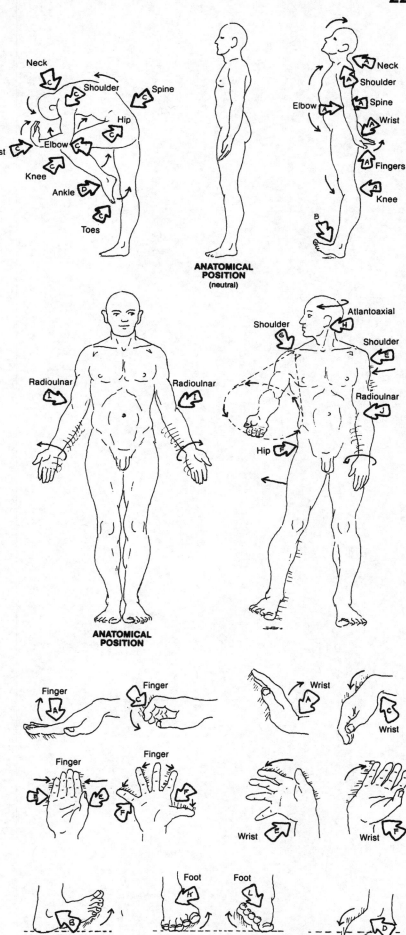

BONES OF THE SKULL (1)

8 CRANIAL

OCCIPITAL A 2 PARIETAL B FRONTAL C

2 TEMPORAL D ETHMOID E SPHENOID F

14 FACIAL

2 NASAL G VOMER H 2 LACRIMAL I

2 ZYGOMATIC J 2 PALATINE K 2 MAXILLA L

MANDIBLE M 2 INFERIOR NASAL CONCHA N

CN: Save the brightest colors for the smallest bones and the lightest colors for the largest. (1) Color one bone in as many views as it appears before going on to the next. (2) There are some very small bones to color in the orbits and in the lower part of the posterior view of the skull. Study these areas carefully before coloring to determine the color boundaries. (3) Do not color the darkened areas in the orbits and nasal cavity in the anterior view.

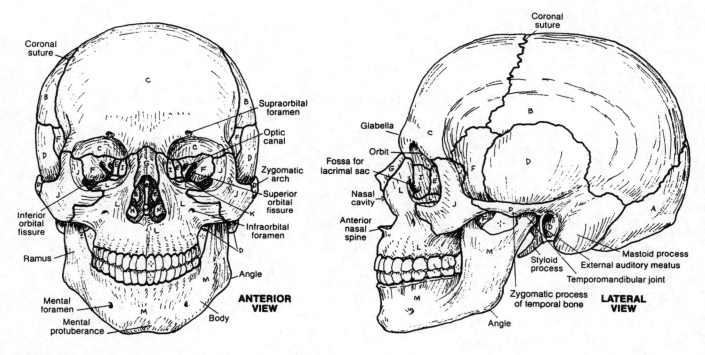

The skull is composed of *cranial bones* (forming a vault for the brain) and *facial bones* (giving origin to the muscles of facial expression and providing buttresses protecting the brain). Except for the temporomandibular joint (a synovial joint), all bones are connected by generally immovable fibrous sutures.

The orbit is composed of seven bones, has three significant fissures/canals, and is home to the eye and related muscles, nerves, and vessels. The most delicate of the skull bones is at the medial orbital wall. The external nose is largely cartilaginous and is therefore not part of the bony skull.

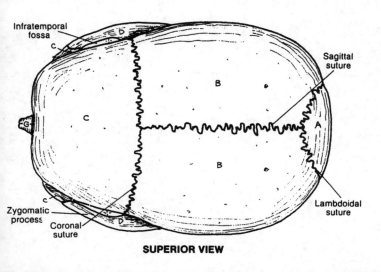

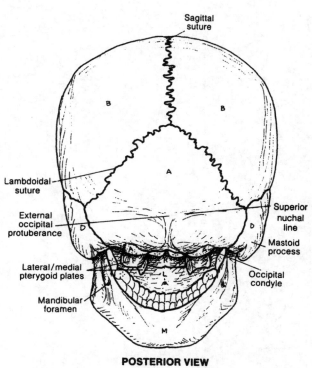

BONES OF THE SKULL (2)

CRANIAL: OCCIPITAL ᴀ PARIETAL ʙ FRONTAL ᴄ
TEMPORAL ᴅ ETHMOID ᴇ SPHENOID ꜰ
FACIAL: NASAL ɢ VOMER ʜ ZYGOMATIC ᴊ PALATINE ᴋ
MAXILLA ʟ INFERIOR NASAL CONCHA ɴ

CN: Use the same colors for these bones as were used on the previous plate. (1) Color the three views simultaneously. (2) In the lower views, pay close attention to the many foramina that are left uncolored. (3) Notice but don't color the small drawing below that summarizes the large fossae of the skull interior to its left. Try to visualize those fossae in the larger view.

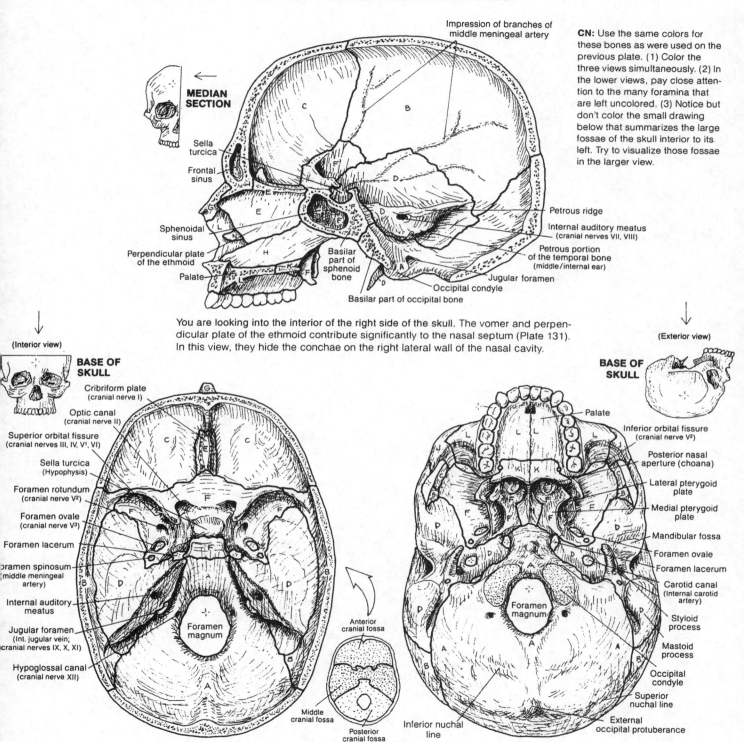

You are looking into the interior of the right side of the skull. The vomer and perpendicular plate of the ethmoid contribute significantly to the nasal septum (Plate 131). In this view, they hide the conchae on the right lateral wall of the nasal cavity.

You are looking onto the floor of the cranial cavity (base of the skull). The anterior cranial fossae support the frontal lobes of the cerebrum (Plate 73); the olfactory tracts lie over the cribriform plates, receiving the olfactory nerves (Plate 100). The middle cranial fossae embrace the temporal lobes; note the numerous foramina/canals for cranial nerves and vessels. The posterior cranial fossa retains the cerebellum and the brain stem (Plate 76) as well as related cranial nerves and vessels that enter or exit the cavity (Plate 83).

The large external surface of the occipital bone is a site of attachment of layers of posterior cervical musculature (Plate 49). The foramen magnum transmits the lower brain stem/spinal cord (Plate 76). The occipital condyles articulate with the facets of the atlas or first cervical vertebra (Plate 28). The muscular pharyngeal wall attaches around the posterior nasal apertures (Plate 139).

VERTEBRAL COLUMN

CN: Use gray for D, yellow for H, and light colors for the rest, especially C, T, L, S, and Co. L4 and L5 represent the lumbar vertebrae most involved in motion. (1) Begin with regions of the column and the three examples of vertebral disorders at lower left. (2) Color the motion segment and its role in flexion and extension. (3) Color the vertebral foramina and canal. (4) Color the example of a protruding intervertebral disc pressing on a spinal nerve.

The vertebral column has 24 individual vertebrae arranged in *cervical, thoracic,* and *lumbar* regions; the *sacral* and *coccygeal* vertebrae are fused (sacrum/coccyx). Numbers of vertebrae in each region are remarkably constant; rarely S1 may be free or L5 may be fused to the sacrum (transitional vertebrae). The seven mobile cervical vertebrae support the neck and the 3–4 kg (6–8 lb) head. The cervical spine is normally curved (*cervical lordosis*) secondary to the development of postural reflexes about three months after birth. The 12 thoracic vertebrae support the thorax, head, and neck. They articulate with 12 ribs bilaterally. The thoracic spine is congenitally curved (*kyphosis*) as shown.

The five lumbar vertebrae support the upper body,

torso, and low back. The column of these vertebrae becomes curved (*lumbar lordosis*) at the onset of walking at 1–2 years of age. The sacrum is the keystone of a weightbearing arch involving the hip bones. The sacral/coccygeal curve is congenital. The variably numbered 1–5 coccygeal vertebrae are usually fused, although the first vertebra may be movable.

Vertebral curvatures may be affected (usually exaggerated) by posture, activity, obesity, pregnancy, trauma, and/or disease; these conditions are given the same names as the normal curves. A slight lateral curvature to the spine often reflects dominant handedness; a significant, possibly disabling, lateral curve (*scoliosis*) may occur for many reasons.

REGIONS
CERVICAL c
THORACIC t
LUMBAR l
SACRAL s
COCCYGEAL co

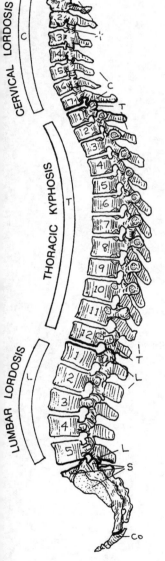

CERVICAL LORDOSIS

THORACIC KYPHOSIS

LUMBAR LORDOSIS

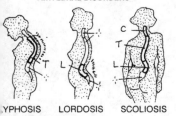

VERTEBRAL DISORDERS

KYPHOSIS LORDOSIS SCOLIOSIS

MOTION SEGMENT
VERTEBRA l⁴
JOINTS:
INTERVERTEBRAL DISC a
POSTERIOR (FACET) b
LIGAMENT d*
VERTEBRA l⁵

VERTEBRAL FORAMEN e
VERTEBRAL CANAL e'
INTERVERTEBRAL FORAMEN f

Each pair of individual, unfused vertebrae constitutes a *motion segment*, the basic movable unit of the back. Combined movements of motion segments underlie movement of the neck and the middle and low back. Each pair of vertebrae in a motion segment, except C1–C2, is attached by three joints: a partly movable, *intervertebral disc* anteriorly and a pair of gliding synovial *facet* (zygapophyseal) *joints* posteriorly. *Ligaments* secure the bones together and encapsulate the facet joints (joint capsules). The *vertebral* or *neural canal*, a series of *vertebral foramina*, transmits the spinal cord and related coverings, vessels, and nerve roots. Located bilaterally between each pair of vertebral pedicles are passageways, each called an *intervertebral foramen*, transmitting spinal nerves, their coverings/vessels, and some vessels to the spinal cord.

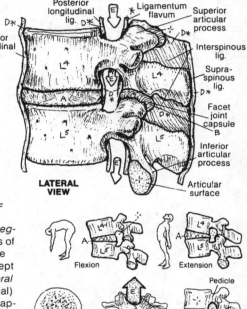

Posterior longitudinal lig. · Ligamentum flavum · Superior articular process
Anterior longitudinal lig.
L4
L4
Interspinous lig.
Supraspinous lig.
Facet joint capsule B
L5
L5
Inferior articular process
Articular surface

LATERAL VIEW

Flexion Extension

Pedicle
Superior view Posterior view Lateral view Pedicle

INTERVERTEBRAL DISC a
ANNULUS FIBROSUS a'
NUCLEUS PULPOSUS g
SPINAL NERVE h

The intervertebral disc consists of the *annulus fibrosus* (concentric, interwoven collagenous fibers integrated with cartilage cells) attached to the vertebral bodies above and below, and the more central *nucleus pulposus* (a mass of degenerated collagen, proteoglycans, and water). The discs make possible movement between vertebral bodies. With aging, the discs dehydrate and thin, resulting in a loss of height. The cervical and lumbar discs, particularly, are subject to early degeneration from one or more of a number of causes. Weakening and/or tearing of the annulus can result in a broad-based bulge or a localized (focal) protrusion of the nucleus and adjacent annulus; such an event can compress a *spinal nerve* root as shown.

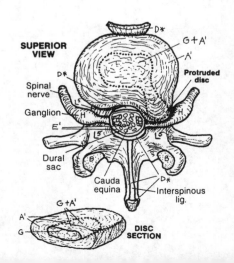

SUPERIOR VIEW

G+A'
A'
Protruded disc
Spinal nerve
Ganglion
Dural sac
Cauda equina
Interspinous lig.

DISC SECTION

CERVICAL & THORACIC VERTEBRAE

CN: Use red for M and use the same colors as were used on Plate 21 for C and T. Use dark colors for N, O, and R. (1) Begin with the parts of a cervical vertebra. Color the atlas and axis and note they have been given separate colors to distinguish them from other cervical vertebrae. (2) Color the parts of a thoracic vertebra and then the thoracic portion of the vertebral column. Note the three different facet/demifacet colors.

CERVICAL VERTEBRA c
BODY c'
PEDICLE B
TRANSVERSE PROCESS G
ARTICULAR PROCESS H
FACET H'
LAMINA I
SPINOUS PROCESS J

ATLAS K
AXIS L

Cranium *See 20*

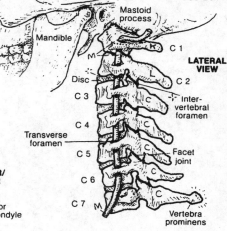

LATERAL VIEW

Mastoid process · Mandible · C 1 · Disc · C 2 · C 3 · Intervertebral foramen · C 4 · Transverse foramen · C 5 · Facet joint · C 6 · C 7 · Vertebra prominens

VERTEBRAL ARTERY M

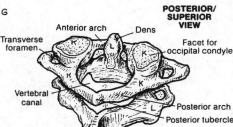

POSTERIOR/ SUPERIOR VIEW

Anterior arch · Dens · Transverse foramen · Facet for occipital condyle · Vertebral canal · Posterior arch · Posterior tubercle · Bifid spine

Transverse foramen · Vertebral foramen · Bifid spine

SUPERIOR VIEW

TYPICAL CERVICAL (C4) VERTEBRA

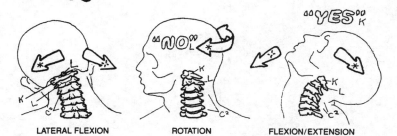

"YES" K

"NO" L · "YES" K

LATERAL FLEXION **ROTATION** **FLEXION/EXTENSION**

The small seven cervical vertebrae support and move the head and neck, supported by ligaments and strap-like paracervical (paraspinal) muscles. The ring-shaped *atlas* (C 1) has no body; thus there are no weight-bearing discs between the occiput and C1, and between C1 and C2 (the *axis*). Head weight is transferred to C3 by the large *articular processes* and *facets* of C1 and C2. The atlantooccipital joints, in conjunction with the C3–C7 facet joints, permit a remarkable degree of flexion/extension ("yes" movements). The dens of C2 projects into the anterior part of the C1 ring, forming a pivot joint, enabling the head and C1 to rotate up to 80° ("no" movements). Such rotational capacity is permitted by the relatively horizontal orientation of the cervical facets. The C3–C6 vertebrae are similar; C7 is remarkable for its prominent *spinous process*, easily palpated. The anteriorly directed cervical curve and the extensive paracervical musculature preclude palpation of the other cervical spinous processes. The *vertebral arteries*, enroute to the brain stem, pass through foramina of the *transverse processes* of the upper six cervical vertebrae. These vessels are subject to stretching injuries with extreme cervical rotation of the hyperextended neck. The cervical vertebral canal conducts the cervical spinal cord and its coverings (not shown). The C4–C5 and C5–C6 motion segments are the most mobile of the cervical region and are particularly prone to disc/facet degeneration.

The twelve thoracic vertebrae—characterized by long, slender spinous processes, heart-shaped *bodies*, and nearly vertically oriented *facets*—articulate with *ribs* bilaterally. In general, each rib forms a synovial joint with two *demifacets* on the bodies of adjacent vertebrae and a single *facet* on the transverse process of the lower vertebra. Variations of these costovertebral joints are seen with T1, T11, and T12.

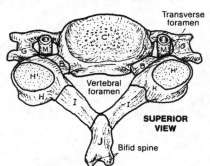

LATERAL VIEW

Disc

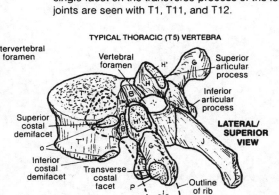

Intervertebral foramen

T 1 · T 2 · T 3 · T 4 · T 5 · T 6 · T 7 · T 8 · T 9 · T 10 · T 11 · T 12

TYPICAL THORACIC (T5) VERTEBRA

Vertebral foramen · Superior articular process · Inferior articular process · Superior costal demifacet · Inferior costal demifacet · Transverse costal facet · Outline of rib

LATERAL/ SUPERIOR VIEW

THORACIC VERTEBRA T
BODY T'
FACET N
DEMIFACET O
TRANSVERSE FACET P
RIB Q
LIGAMENT R*

LUMBAR, SACRAL & COCCYGEAL VERTEBRAE

CN: Use the same colors as were used on the previous two plates for C, T, L, E, F, A, S, and Co. (1) Begin with the three large views of lumbar vertebrae. (2) Color the different planes of articular facets. (3) Color the four views of the sacrum and coccyx. Note that the central portion of the median section receives the vertebral canal color (E¹).

LUMBAR VERTEBRA L
VERTEBRAL FORAMEN E
VERTEBRAL CANAL E'
INTERVERTEBRAL FORAMEN F
INTERVERTEBRAL DISC A

The five lumbar vertebrae are the most massive of all the individual vertebrae, their thick processes securing the attachments of numerous ligaments and muscles/tendons. Significant flexion and extension of the lumbar and lumbosacral motion segments, particularly at L4–L5 and L5–S1, are possible. At about L1, the spinal cord terminates and the cauda equina (bundle of lumbar, sacral, and coccygeal nerve roots; see Plate 70) begins. The lumbar *intervertebral foramina* are large. Transiting nerve roots/sheaths take up only about 50% of the volume of these foramina. Disc and facet degeneration is common in the L4–L5 and L5–S1 segments; reduction of space for the nerve roots increases the risk of nerve root irritation/compression. Occasionally, the L5 vertebra is partially or completely fused to the sacrum (sacralized L5). The S1 vertebra may be partially or wholly non-fused (lumbarized S1), resulting in essentially six lumbar vertebrae and a sacrum of four fused vertebrae.

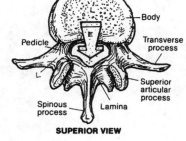

SUPERIOR VIEW

Body
Transverse process
Pedicle
Superior articular process
Spinous process
Lamina

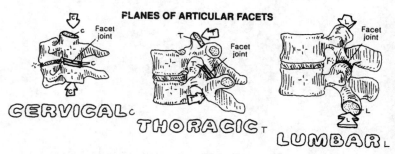

PLANES OF ARTICULAR FACETS

Facet joint

CERVICAL c
THORACIC T
LUMBAR L

Facet joint

The planes (orientation) of the articular facets determine the direction and influence the degree of motion segment movement. The plane of the *cervical facets* is angled coronally off the horizontal plane about 30°. Considerable freedom of movement of the cervical spine is permitted in all planes (sagittal, coronal, horizontal). The *thoracic facets* lie more vertically in the coronal plane and are virtually non-weightbearing. The range of motion here is significantly limited in all planes, less so in rotation. The plane of the *lumbar facets* is largely sagittal, resisting rotation of the lumbar spine, transitioning to a more coronal orientation at L5–S1. The L4–L5 facet joints permit the greatest degree of lumbar motion in all planes.

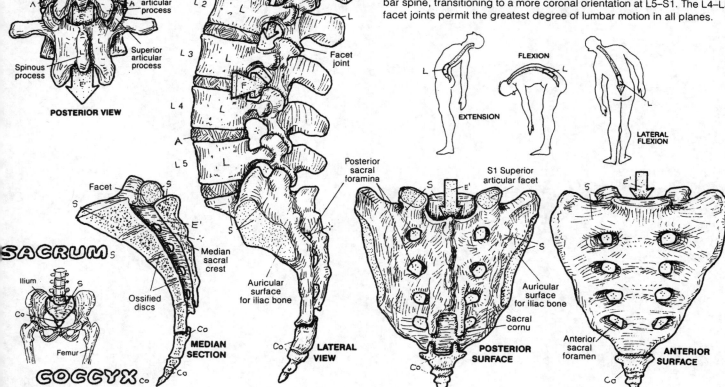

Superior articular process facet
Transverse process
Body
Inferior articular process
Superior articular process
Spinous process

POSTERIOR VIEW

L1 Superior articular process
L1 Inferior articular process
L1
L2
L3
Facet joint
L4
L5

FLEXION
EXTENSION
LATERAL FLEXION

SACRUM S
Facet
Ilium
Co
Femur
COCCYX Co

Median sacral crest
Ossified discs
MEDIAN SECTION

Posterior sacral foramina
Auricular surface for iliac bone
LATERAL VIEW

S1 Superior articular facet
Auricular surface for iliac bone
Sacral cornu
POSTERIOR SURFACE

Anterior sacral foramen
ANTERIOR SURFACE

The sacrum consists of five fused vertebrae; the intervertebral discs are largely replaced by bone. The sacral (vertebral) canal contains the terminal sac of the dura mater (dural sac, thecal sac) to S2 and the sacral nerve roots, which transit the sacral foramina. The sacrum joins with the ilium of the hip bone at the auricular surface, forming the sacroiliac joint.

The sacrum and the ilia of the hip bones form an arch for the transmission and distribution of weightbearing forces to the heads of the femora. It is a strong arch, and the sacrum is its keystone. The coccyx consists of 2–4 tiny individual or partly fused, rudimentary vertebrae. The first coccygeal vertebra is the most completely developed.

WRIST AND HAND BONES & JOINTS

CN: Use light colors other than those used for the three arm bones on the previous plates for I and J, light blue for K. (1) Color the three views of the hand and wrist: note the callouts identifying the joints that contribute to the movements shown in the satellite sketches. (2) Color the major ligaments of the wrist joints gray. Numerous carpal and phalangeal ligaments are not shown. (3) In the sectional view, color the bones and their articular cartilage (L). Color the synovial cavities (L with dark outlines) of the wrist black, but not the intercarpal joint cavities.

8 CARPALS:
SCAPHOID_A LUNATE_B TRIQUETRUM_C PISIFORM_D
TRAPEZIUM_E TRAPEZOID_F CAPITATE_G HAMATE_H

5 METACARPALS_I 14 PHALANGES_J

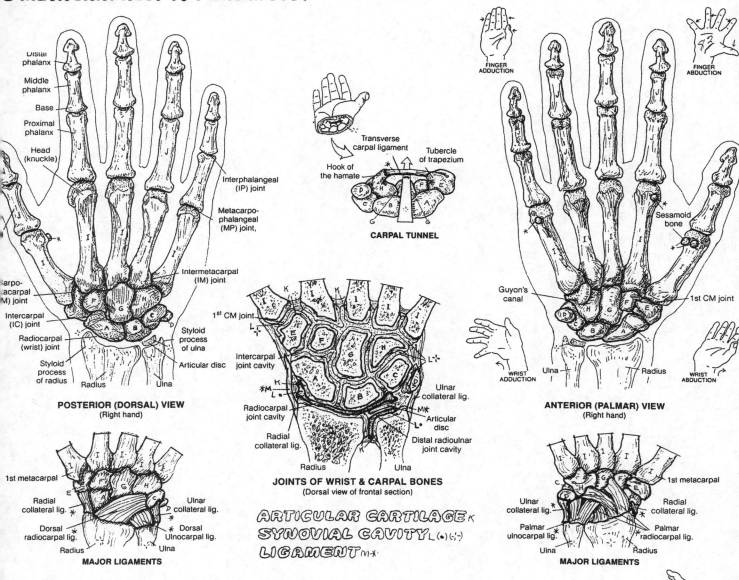

Distal phalanx
Middle phalanx
Base
Proximal phalanx
Head (knuckle)
Interphalangeal (IP) joint
Metacarpophalangeal (MP) joint,
Intermetacarpal (IM) joint
Carpometacarpal (CM) joint
Intercarpal (IC) joint
Radiocarpal (wrist) joint
Styloid process of radius
Styloid process of ulna
Articular disc
Radius
Ulna

POSTERIOR (DORSAL) VIEW
(Right hand)

Transverse carpal ligament
Hook of the hamate
Tubercle of trapezium

CARPAL TUNNEL

1st CM joint
Intercarpal joint cavity
Radiocarpal joint cavity
Radial collateral lig.
Radius
Ulnar collateral lig.
Articular disc
Distal radioulnar joint cavity
Ulna

JOINTS OF WRIST & CARPAL BONES
(Dorsal view of frontal section)

ARTICULAR CARTILAGE_K
SYNOVIAL CAVITY_L (•)(÷)
LIGAMENT_M-×

Sesamoid bone
Guyon's canal
1st CM joint
Ulna
Radius

ANTERIOR (PALMAR) VIEW
(Right hand)

FINGER ADDUCTION
FINGER ABDUCTION
WRIST ADDUCTION
WRIST ABDUCTION

1st metacarpal
Radial collateral lig.
Dorsal radiocarpal lig.
Radius
Ulnar collateral lig.
Dorsal Ulnocarpal lig.
Ulna

MAJOR LIGAMENTS

1st metacarpal
Ulnar collateral lig.
Palmar ulnocarpal lig.
Ulna
Radial collateral lig.
Palmar radiocarpal lig.
Radius

MAJOR LIGAMENTS

The wrist joint (synovial; biaxial) is formed by the distal articular surface of the radius with the articular surfaces of the *scaphoid* and *lunate bones* primarily, and between the articular disc and the *triquetrum* secondarily. Movements here are flexion, extension, adduction, and abduction. The *wrist joint* and *carpal joints* are secured by palmar and dorsal radiocarpal and ulnocarpal ligaments and by radial and ulnar collateral ligaments. The *intercarpal joints*, between the proximal and distal rows of carpal bones, contribute to wrist movement. The trough between the *hamate* and *trapezium* bones anteriorly provides a carpal tunnel for the passage of the long flexor tendons to the thumb and fingers

as well as the median nerve. Compression by the transverse carpal ligament can irritate or depress the function of the median nerve (numbness to three radial fingers; thumb weakness). Guyon's canal transmits the ulnar artery and nerve.

Hand movement involves movements of the metacarpophalangeal (MP) and interphalangeal (IP) joints primarily, and among the carpometacarpal and intermetacarpal joints secondarily—with one exception: the unique first carpometacarpal (CM) joint (synovial; saddle). Notice the mobility it gives the thumb, as in opposing thumb and little finger, and circumduction of the thumb.

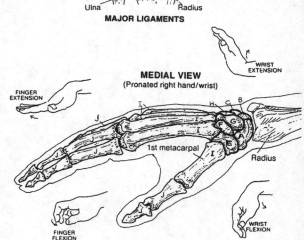

MEDIAL VIEW
(Pronated right hand/wrist)

WRIST EXTENSION
FINGER EXTENSION
1st metacarpal
Radius
FINGER FLEXION
WRIST FLEXION

INTRODUCTION TO SKELETAL MUSCLE

CN: Use light colors for A–E. (1) Begin with the muscle belly and tendons in the upper illustration. (2) When coloring the narrow borders of the endomysium (C) in the enlarged section, it is recommended that you also color over the muscle fiber ends (D) with the very light endomysium color, and then go back over the fiber ends with a darker color (D). Do not color the neurovascular bundle, or the cut ends of blood vessels and capillaries. (3) Color the lower illustration.

SKELETAL MUSCLE
BELLY A
FASCIA:
EPIMYSIUM A'
PERIMYSIUM B
ENDOMYSIUM C
MUSCLE FIBER (CELL) D
TENDON E

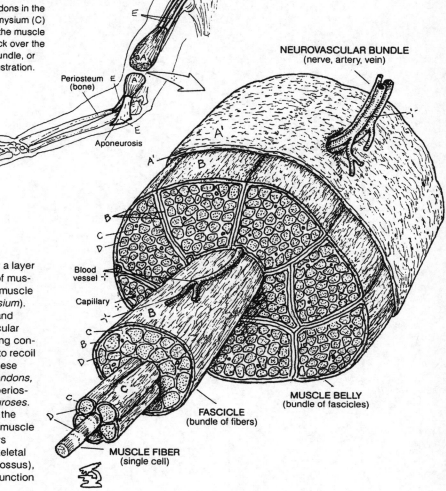

NEUROVASCULAR BUNDLE
(nerve, artery, vein)

Periosteum
(bone)

Aponeurosis

Blood vessel

Capillary

MUSCLE BELLY
(bundle of fascicles)

FASCICLE
(bundle of fibers)

MUSCLE FIBER
(single cell)

A named skeletal muscle (e.g., biceps brachii), surrounded by a layer of deep fascia (*epimysium*), consists of fascicles or bundles of muscle fibers enveloped in thin fibrous tissue (*perimysium*). Each muscle fiber is surrounded by a thin sheath of fibrous tissue (*endomysium*). Each of these fibrous layers is important to muscle structure and function, providing support for nerves and vessels (neurovascular bundles), ensuring uniform distribution of muscle tension during contraction, and maintaining the elasticity of muscle, permitting it to recoil to its resting length following stretching. It is the merging of these fibrous layers at the ends of the muscle fibers that forms the *tendons*, which integrate the muscle to its attachment site(s), such as periosteum or another tendon. Broad, flat tendons are called *aponeuroses*. The mass of the fasciae-enveloped contractile fibers is called the *belly* of the muscle. It is the muscle belly that shortens during muscle contraction. The belly may be shaped one of a number of ways depending on its tendinous arrangement and attachments. Skeletal muscles are named in relation to their attachments (e.g., hyoglossus), shape (e.g., trapezius), number of heads (e.g., quadriceps), function (e.g., adductor magnus), or position (e.g., brachialis).

MECHANICS OF MOVEMENT
FULCRUM F (JOINT) F'
EFFORT A (MUSCLE) A
RESISTANCE G (WEIGHT) G'

Skeletal muscles employ simple machines, such as levers, to increase the efficiency of their contractile work about a joint. Mechanically, the degree of *muscular effort* required to overcome resistance to movement at a *joint* (fulcrum) depends upon the force of that resistance (*weight*); the relative distances from the anatomical fulcrum to the anatomical sites of *muscular effort*; and the anatomical sites of *resistance* (joints). The position of the joint relative to the site of muscle pull and the site of imposed load determines the class of the lever system in use.

1ST CLASS LEVER

In a 1st class lever, the joint lies between the muscle and the load. This is the most efficient class of lever. By flexing the neck and posturing the head forward and downward, the load (G^1) is appreciably increased (due to gravity), and the muscular effort (A) to hold that posture may induce muscle pain and stiffness/tightness (overuse).

2ND CLASS LEVER

In a 2nd class lever, the load lies between the joint and the pulling muscle. This lever system operates in lifting a wheelbarrow (the wheel is the fulcrum) as well as lifting a 75 kg (165 lb) body onto the metatarsal heads at the metatarsophalangeal joints. This is a relatively easy task for the strong calf (triceps surae) muscles; but try standing on the heads of your middle phalanges (increasing the distance F^1-G^1)!

3RD CLASS LEVER

In a 3rd class lever, the muscle lies between the joint and the load and has a poor mechanical advantage here. Consider the difference in muscular effort required to carry a 45 kg (100 lb) bag of cement in your hands with flexed elbows (elbow joint: 3rd class lever) and carrying your 75 kg (165 lb) body on the heads of your metatarsals (2nd class lever at the metatarsophalangeal joints). It is all a matter of leverage.

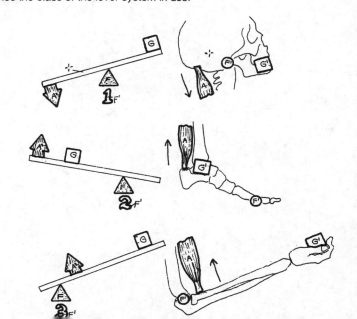

INTEGRATION OF MUSCLE ACTION

CN: Use a bright color for A and a light one for E. (1) Color the small arrows and the large letters of origin (O) and insertion (I) adjacent to the examples of contracted and stretched muscles. (2) In the lower illustration, color the portions of pronator teres and pronator quadratus that are outlined by dotted lines. These parts of the muscles are normally concealed by the radius in this lateral view.

Skeletal muscle generally connects two bones and crosses the joint between those two bones. When the muscle shortens (contracts), the two bones come closer together, isometric contraction excepted. Muscles never push; they always pull. In any given movement between two bones, one bone is generally fixed, and the other moves. The muscle attachment at the fixed bone is the *origin;* the attachment at the moving bone is the *insertion.* In complex movements where it is difficult to identify a "fixed" bone, the origin of the muscle is the more proximal attachment.

When a muscle contracts across a joint, other muscles crossing that joint are affected. No one muscle acts alone in joint movement. In flexion of the elbow joint, for example, biceps brachii (and brachialis, not shown) *contract*s, while triceps brachii is *stretched.* Conversely, in elbow extension, triceps is contracted, and the biceps/brachialis muscles are stretched. In neutral, all three are *relaxed*(at rest). Tense (contracted) muscles can often be relaxed by gentle stretching.

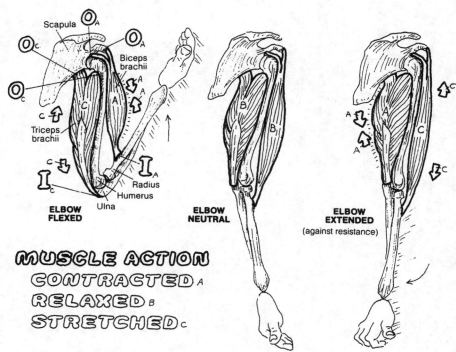

ELBOW FLEXED — ELBOW NEUTRAL — ELBOW EXTENDED (against resistance)

MUSCLE ACTION
CONTRACTED A
RELAXED B
STRETCHED C

ACTORS IN ELBOW FLEXION

No muscle acts alone in the movement of a joint. In the movements shown at right, various muscles are functionally integrated in the simple act of lifting an object, with the forearm supinated in the first case and pronated in the second case.

PRIME MOVER (AGONIST) A'

The primary muscle effecting a desired joint movement is called the *prime mover* (agonist). There may be more than one; in elbow flexion with the forearm supinated, brachialis and biceps brachii are both prime movers; biceps adds significantly to the lifting power because of the added work in supinating the radius during elbow flexion. With the forearm pronated and supination resisted, the biceps loses that supinating power, and brachialis, unaffected by a pronated forearm, becomes the prime mover.

ANTAGONIST C'

Muscles that potentially or actually oppose or resist a certain movement are called *antagonists.* In the illustrations at right, triceps is the antagonist in the act of elbow flexion, even though it is being stretched and is not contracted in the case illustrated.

FIXATOR D

Fixator muscles stabilize the more proximal joints during weightbearing functions of the more distal joints. Here the trapezius muscle contracts to stabilize (immobilize) the scapula, creating a rigid platform (the scapula) for operation of the weightbearing, ipsilateral limb.

NEUTRALIZER (SYNERGIST) E

In undertaking a desired and specific movement, undesired movements are resisted by *neutralizers* (*synergists*). During flexion of the elbow with a pronated forearm, pronators of the forearm (pronator quadratus, pronator teres) contract to resist or neutralize supination of the forearm. In this action, the pronators are synergistic with the desired movement.

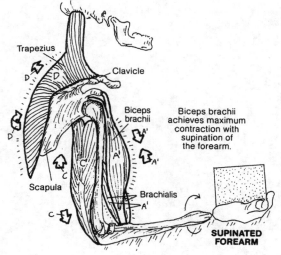

Biceps brachii achieves maximum contraction with supination of the forearm.

SUPINATED FOREARM

ACTORS IN ELBOW FLEXION
(With supination vs. pronation)

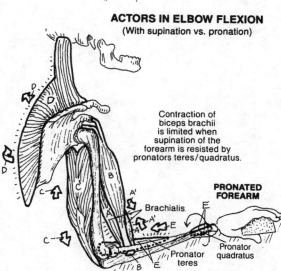

Contraction of biceps brachii is limited when supination of the forearm is resisted by pronators teres/quadratus.

PRONATED FOREARM

Globally integrated and harmonious muscle functioning makes possible painless, rhythmic, and dynamic movements, best revealed in such activities as dance, sports, and exercise. Joints affected by tense or weak interacting muscles, induced by mechanically disadvantaged posture/gait, can be subject to painful and limited movements.

ANTERIOR & LATERAL MUSCLES

CN: Except for Band E, use your lightest colors throughout the plate. (1) Begin with the diagrams of the triangles of the neck and the sternocleidomastoid (A, B, C). Color over all the muscles within the triangles. (2) Then work top and bottom illustrations simultaneously, coloring each muscle in as many views as you can find it. Note the relationship between muscle name and attachment.

The neck is a complex tubular region of muscles, viscera, vessels, and nerves surrounding the cervical vertebrae. The muscles of the neck are arranged in superficial and deep groups. Here we concentrate on superficial muscles. The most superficial posterior and posterolateral muscle of the neck is trapezius (Plate 54). The deep posterior muscles are covered in Plate 49. The most superficial anterior muscle of the neck is platysma (Plate 46). The anterior and lateral muscle groups are divided into triangular areas by the *sternocleidomastoid* muscle.

ANTERIOR TRIANGLE A

SUPRAHYOID MUSCLES D-
STYLOHYOID D' DIGASTRIC D²
MYLOHYOID D³ HYOGLOSSUS D⁴
GENIOHYOID D⁵

HYOID BONE E

INFRAHYOID MUSCLES F-
STERNOHYOID F' OMOHYOID F²
THYROHYOID F³ STERNOTHYROID F⁴

The anterior region of the neck is divided in the midline; each half forms an *anterior triangle*. The borders of the anterior triangle of superficial neck muscles are clearly illustrated. The *hyoid bone*, suspended from the styloid processes of the skull by the stylohyoid ligaments, divides each anterior triangle into upper *suprahyoid* and lower *infrahyoid* regions.

The suprahyoid muscles arise from the tongue (glossus), mandible (mylo-, genio-, anterior digastric), and skull (stylo-, posterior digastric) and insert on the hyoid bone. They elevate the hyoid bone, influencing the movements of the floor of the mouth and the tongue, especially during swallowing. With a fixed hyoid, the suprahyoid muscles, especially the digastrics, depress the mandible.

The infrahyoid muscles generally arise from the sternum, thyroid cartilage of the larynx, or the scapula (omo-) and insert on the hyoid bone. These muscles partially resist elevation of the hyoid bone during swallowing. *Thyrohyoid* elevates the larynx during production of high-pitched sounds; sternohyoid depresses the larynx to assist in production of low-pitched sounds.

POSTERIOR TRIANGLE C

SEMISPINALIS CAPITIS C'
SPLENIUS CAPITIS C²
LEVATOR SCAPULAE C³
SCALENUS: ANT. C⁴ MED. C⁵ POST. C⁶

The posterior triangle consists of an array of muscles covered by a layer of deep (investing) cervical fascia just under the skin between sternocleidomastoid and trapezius. The borders of the triangle are clearly illustrated. Muscles of this region arise from the skull and cervical vertebrae; they descend to and insert upon the upper two ribs (*scalenes*), the upper scapula (*omohyoid, levator scapulae*), and the cervical/thoracic vertebral spines (*splenius capitis, semispinalis capitis*). These muscles' function becomes clear when you visualize their attachments.

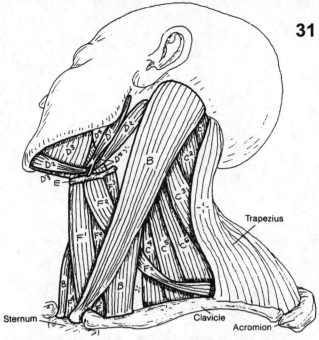

STERNOCLEIDOMASTOID B

The sternocleidomastoid muscle, acting unilaterally, tilts the head laterally on the same side while simultaneously rotating the head and pulling the back of the head downward, lifting the chin, and rotating the front of the head to the opposite side. Both muscle bellies acting together move the head forward (anteriorly) while extending the upper cervical vertebrae, lifting the chin upward.

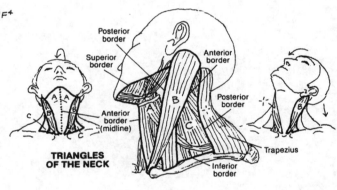

TRIANGLES OF THE NECK

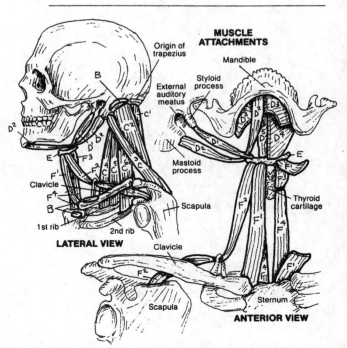

LATERAL VIEW

MUSCLE ATTACHMENTS

ANTERIOR VIEW

DEEP MUSCLES OF BACK & POSTERIOR NECK

CN: Use your lightest colors on the B and C groups. Note that splenius (A) and semispinalis (C^1) represent more than one muscle; the muscle subsets are identified. (1) After coloring the muscles of the back and posterior neck, color the lower right diagram, which describes the location and function of the deep movers of the spine.

The deep muscles of the back and posterior neck extend, rotate, or laterally flex one or more of the 24 paired facet joints and the 22 intervertebral disc joints of the vertebral column. The long muscles move several motion segments (recall Plate 27) with one contraction, while the short muscles can move one or two motion segments at a time (see intrinsic movers).

COVERING MUSCLE

SPLENIUS A

The splenius muscles extend and rotate the neck and head in concert with the opposite sternocleidomastoid muscle. Splenius capitis covers the deeper muscles of the upper spine.

VERTICAL MUSCLES

ERECTOR SPINAE B
SPINALIS B'
LONGISSIMUS B²
ILIOCOSTALIS B³

The erector spinae group comprises the principal extensors of the vertebral motion segments. Oriented vertically along the longitudinal axis of the back, they are thick, quadrilateral muscles in the lumbar region, splitting into smaller, thinner separate bundles attaching to the ribs (iliocostalis), and upper vertebrae and head (longissimus, spinalis). Erector spinae arises from the lower thoracic and lumbar spines, the sacrum, ilium, and intervening ligaments.

OBLIQUE MUSCLES

TRANSVERSOSPINALIS GROUP C
SEMISPINALIS C'
MULTIFIDUS C²
ROTATORES C³

The transversospinalis group extends the motion segments of the back, and rotates the thoracic and cervical vertebral joints. These muscles generally run from the transverse processes of one vertebra to the spine of the vertebra above, spanning three or more vertebrae. The semispinales are the largest muscles of this group, reaching from mid-thorax to the posterior skull; the multifidi consist of deep fasciculi spanning 1–3 motion segments from sacrum to C2; the rotatores are well defined only in the thoracic region.

DEEPEST MUSCLES

INTERTRANSVERSARII D
INTERSPINALIS E
SUBOCCIPITAL MUSCLES F

These small, deep-lying muscles cross the joints of only one motion segment. They are collectively major postural muscles. Electromyographic evidence has shown that these short muscles remain in sustained contraction for long periods of time during movement and standing/sitting postures. They are most prominent in the cervical and lumbar regions. The small muscles set deep in the posterior, suboccipital region (deep to semispinalis and erector spinae) rotate and extend the joints between the skull and C1 and C2 vertebrae.

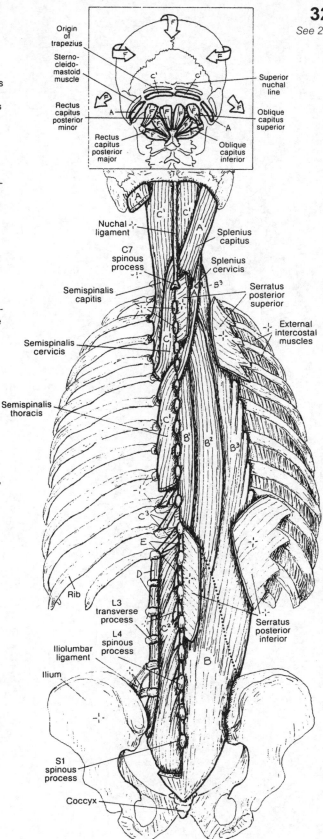

Origin of trapezius
Sterno-cleido-mastoid muscle
Rectus capitus posterior minor
Rectus capitus posterior major
Superior nuchal line
Oblique capitus superior
Oblique capitus inferior
Nuchal ligament
Splenius capitus
C7 spinous process
Splenius cervicis
Semispinalis capitis
Serratus posterior superior
Semispinalis cervicis
External intercostal muscles
Semispinalis thoracis
Rib
L3 transverse process
L4 spinous process
Iliolumbar ligament
Serratus posterior inferior
Ilium
S1 spinous process
Coccyx

INTRINSIC MOVERS

EXTENSOR E
ROTATOR C³
LATERAL FLEXOR D

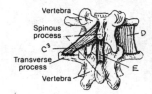

Vertebra
Spinous process
Transverse process
Vertebra

MUSCLES OF THORAX & POSTERIOR ABDOMINAL WALL

CN: Use blue for E and red for G. (1) You may wish to darken the underside of the diaphragm (A) in the anterior view. Do not confuse the arcuate ligaments with the 12th rib. (2) In the cross-sectional view at upper right, color the broken lines that represent transparent, membranous portions of the intercostal muscles.

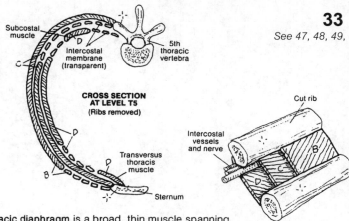

Subcostal muscle
Intercostal membrane (transparent)
5th thoracic vertebra

CROSS SECTION AT LEVEL T5
(Ribs removed)

Transversus thoracis muscle

Sternum

Cut rib

Intercostal vessels and nerve

INTERCOSTAL MUSCLE FIBER ORIENTATION

THORAX MUSCLES +

THORACIC DIAPHRAGM A
EXTERNAL INTERCOSTAL B
INTERNAL INTERCOSTAL C
INNERMOST INTERCOSTAL D

The thoracic diaphragm is a broad, thin muscle spanning the thoracoabdominal cavity; the illustration shows much of its origin (all except the lower six ribs).

The left and right halves of the diaphragm insert into each other (central tendon). The diaphragm is responsible for 75% of the respiratory air flow. Openings (hiatuses) in the diaphragm provide passage for major transiting structures.

The intercostal muscles alter the dimensions of the thoracic cavity by collectively moving the ribs, resulting in 25% of the total respiratory effort. The specific function of each of these muscles, with respect to fiber orientation, is not understood. The innermost intercostals are an inconstant layer, and here include the transversus thoracis and subcostal muscles.

INFERIOR VENA CAVA E
ESOPHAGUS F
AORTA G

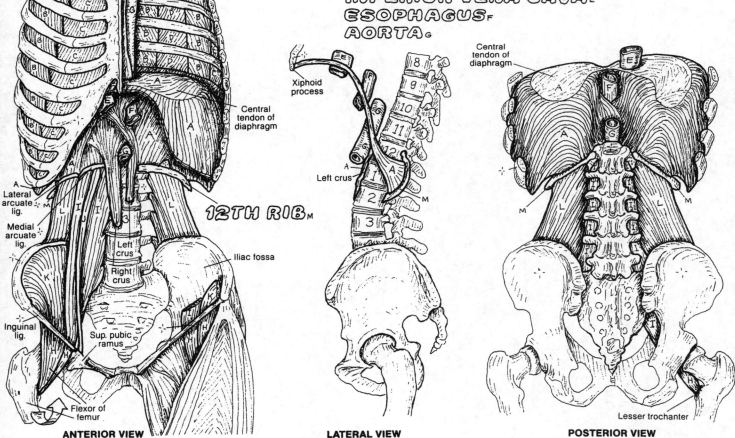

ANTERIOR VIEW

External intercostal membrane (transparent)
Sternum (cut)
Inner view of posterior thorax
Cut rib
Central tendon of diaphragm
Lateral arcuate lig.
Medial arcuate lig.
12TH RIB M
Iliac fossa
Left crus
Right crus
Inguinal lig.
Sup. pubic ramus
Flexor of femur

LATERAL VIEW

Xiphoid process
Left crus

POSTERIOR VIEW

Central tendon of diaphragm
Lesser trochanter

POSTERIOR ABDOMINAL WALL MUSCLES +

ILIOPSOAS H
PSOAS MAJOR I   MINOR J
ILIACUS K
QUADRATUS LUMBORUM L

The tendons of iliacus and psoas major converge to a single insertion (*iliopsoas*). Iliopsoas, a strong flexor of the hip joint, is a powerful flexor of the lumbar vertebrae; a weak psoas may contribute to low back pain. *Quadratus lumborum* is an extensor of the lumbar vertebrae (bilaterally) and a lateral flexor unilaterally. It functions in respiration by securing the 12th rib. Immediately anterior to these muscles is the retroperitoneum (see Plate 147).

MUSCLES OF SCAPULAR STABILIZATION

TRAPEZIUS_A
RHOMBOID MAJOR_B , MINOR_B'
LEVATOR SCAPULAE_C
SERRATUS ANTERIOR_D
PECTORALIS MINOR_E

CN: (1) Color the six muscles of scapular stabilization. Note that the two rhomboids receive the same color (B). In the two main views, color gray the nuchal ligament and its title. (2) Color the attachment site diagrams at upper right. (3) In the illustrations below describing scapular movement, note that the three regions of trapezius (A) play different roles. Color gray the scapulae, the arrows, and the movement titles.

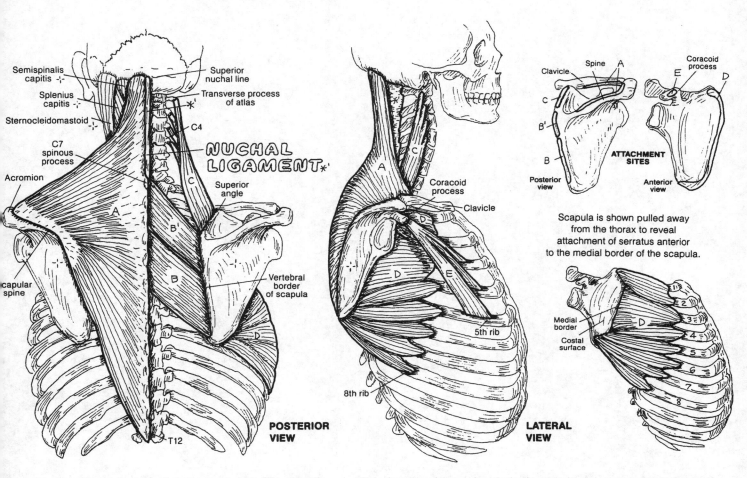

ATTACHMENT SITES

Scapula is shown pulled away from the thorax to reveal attachment of serratus anterior to the medial border of the scapula.

POSTERIOR VIEW

LATERAL VIEW

The scapula lies on the posterior thorax, roughly from T2 to T8. It has no direct bony attachment with the axial skeleton. Enveloped by muscle, it glides over the fascia-covered thorax during upper limb movement (scapulothoracic motion). Bursae have been reported between the thorax and the scapula; so has bursitis. The scapula is dynamically moored to the axial skeleton by muscles attaching the scapula to the axial skeleton. These *muscles of scapular stabilization* make possible considerable scapular mobility and, therefore, shoulder/arm mobility.

Note the roles of these six muscles in scapular movement, and note how the shoulder and arm are affected. *Pectoralis minor* assists *serratus anterior* in protraction of the scapula such as in pushing against a wall; it also helps in depression of the shoulder and downward rotation of the scapula. Consider the power resident in serratus anterior and trapezius in pushing or swinging a bat. Note the especially broad sites of attachment of the *trapezius* muscle. Trapezius commonly manifests significant tension with hard work—mental or physical. A brief massage of this muscle often brings quick relief.

MOVEMENTS OF THE SCAPULA*

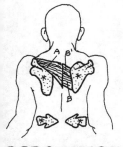

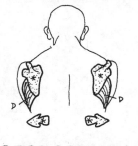

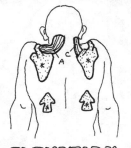

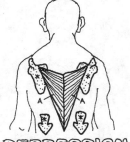

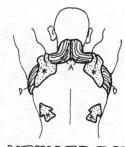

RETRACTION.*
Military posture ("squaring the shoulders")

PROTRACTION.*
Pushing forward with outstretched arms and hands.

ELEVATION*
Shrugging the shoulders or protecting the head.

DEPRESSION*
Straight arms on parallel bars, holding weight.

UPWARD ROT.*
Lifting or reaching over head.

MUSCLES OF MUSCULOTENDINOUS CUFF

CN: (1) In addition to the four muscles, color the arrows and titles describing their actions. (2) Color the muscular attachment sites and the diagram of the function of the cuff muscles at mid-right. (3) Do not color the problem spot numerals in the lower illustration. They are there to identify locations discussed in the text.

SUPRASPINATUS_A
INFRASPINATUS_B
TERES MINOR_C
SUBSCAPULARIS_D

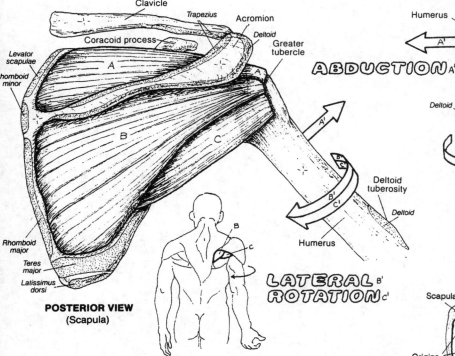

POSTERIOR VIEW
(Scapula)

ABDUCTION A'

LATERAL ROTATION C'

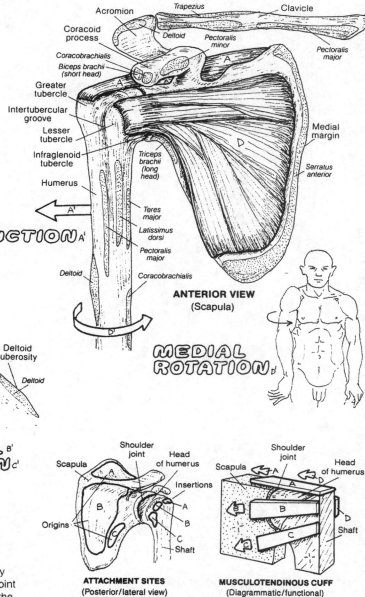

ANTERIOR VIEW
(Scapula)

MEDIAL ROTATION D

ATTACHMENT SITES
(Posterior/lateral view)

MUSCULOTENDINOUS CUFF
(Diagrammatic/functional)

PROBLEM SPOTS IN THE SHOULDER REGION
(Anterior view)

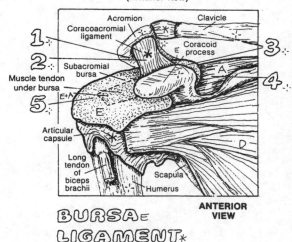

ANTERIOR VIEW

BURSA E
LIGAMENT *

The socket at the glenolhumeral joint (glenoid fossa) is too shallow to offer any bony security for the head of the humerus. As ligaments would severely limit joint movement, muscle tension must be employed to pull the humeral head in to the shallow scapular socket during shoulder movements. Four muscles fulfill this function: *supraspinatus*, *infraspinatus*, *teres minor*, and *subscapularis* ("SITS muscles"). These muscles form a musculotendinous ("rotator") cuff around the head of the humerus, enforcing joint security. Especially effective during robust shoulder movements, they permit the major movers of the joint to work without risking joint dislocation.

The SITS muscles have come to be known as the *"rotator cuff"* muscles, even though one of them, supraspinatus, is an abductor of the shoulder joint and not a rotator. Indeed, among some health care providers, supraspinatus is known as the "rotator cuff" in the context of a "rotator cuff tear."

The shoulder joint and the supraspinatus muscle/tendon are subject to early degeneration from overuse. The problem is generally one of impingement (chronic physical contact and friction) between the acromion (1), the coraco-acromial ligament (2), and the distal clavicle (3) above, and the tendon of supraspinatus (4) and the subacromial bursa (5) below. Those with a down-turned acromion or a previously dislocated, offset acromioclavicular joint are especially vulnerable to impingement (supraspinatus tendinitis and subsequent tearing, subacromial bursitis, limitation of shoulder motion, and pain). All over-head activities (such as those of professional drapery hangers, ceiling plaster-ers, baseball pitchers) and acromial loading (hose-carrying firemen, those carrying heavy purses by straps over the shoulder, mail delivery persons) pursued over a long period can induce changes (bony spurring, bursal destruction) with impingement signs and symptoms.

MOVERS OF SHOULDER JOINT

DELTOID_A PECTORALIS MAJOR_B
LATISSIMUS DORSI_C TERES MAJOR_D
CORACOBRACHIALIS_E BICEPS BRACHII_F
TRICEPS BRACHII (LONG HEAD)_G

CN: (1) Begin with both posterior views; note that the biceps and triceps are not shown on the lateral view.
(2) When coloring the muscles below, note the actions of different parts of the deltoid (A) and pectoralis major (B).

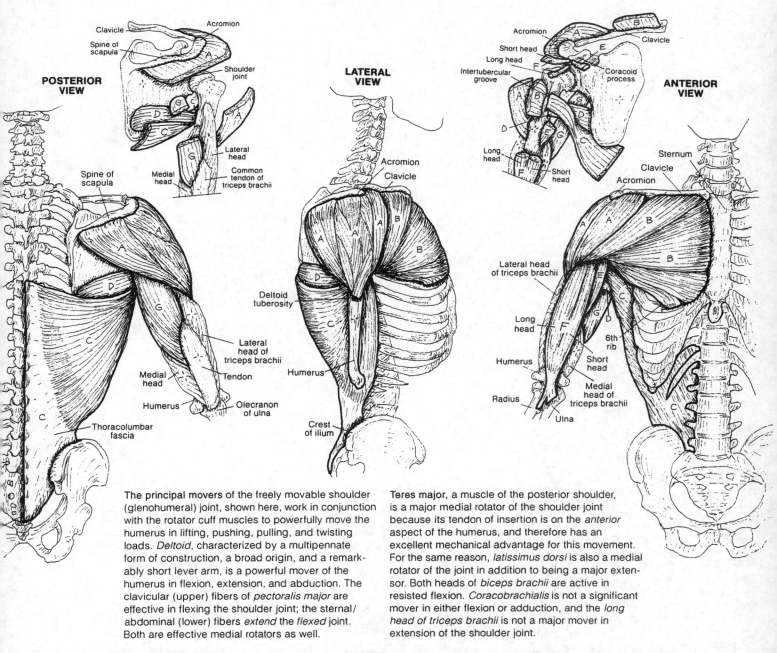

The principal movers of the freely movable shoulder (glenohumeral) joint, shown here, work in conjunction with the rotator cuff muscles to powerfully move the humerus in lifting, pushing, pulling, and twisting loads. *Deltoid*, characterized by a multipennate form of construction, a broad origin, and a remarkably short lever arm, is a powerful mover of the humerus in flexion, extension, and abduction. The clavicular (upper) fibers of *pectoralis major* are effective in flexing the shoulder joint; the sternal/abdominal (lower) fibers *extend* the *flexed* joint. Both are effective medial rotators as well.

Teres major, a muscle of the posterior shoulder, is a major medial rotator of the shoulder joint because its tendon of insertion is on the *anterior* aspect of the humerus, and therefore has an excellent mechanical advantage for this movement. For the same reason, *latissimus dorsi* is also a medial rotator of the joint in addition to being a major extensor. Both heads of *biceps brachii* are active in resisted flexion. *Coracobrachialis* is not a significant mover in either flexion or adduction, and the *long head of triceps brachii* is not a major mover in extension of the shoulder joint.

MOVEMENTS OF THE HUMERUS AT THE SHOULDER JOINT*

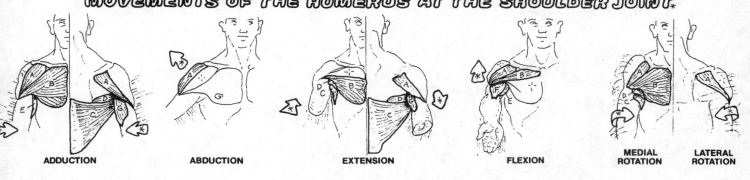

ADDUCTION **ABDUCTION** **EXTENSION** **FLEXION** **MEDIAL ROTATION** **LATERAL ROTATION**

MOVERS OF ELBOW & RADIOULNAR JOINTS

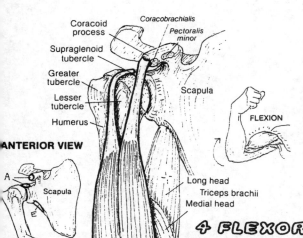

Coracoid process
Coracobrachialis
Pectoralis minor
Supraglenoid tubercle
Greater tubercle
Lesser tubercle
Humerus
Scapula
FLEXION

ANTERIOR VIEW

Scapula
Humerus
Long head
Short head
Radial tuberosity
Ulna
Radius

Long head
Triceps brachii
Medial head

CN: Use the same colors for biceps brachii (A) and triceps brachii (E) as you did for those muscles on Plate 56. (1) Color the four flexors and their attachment sites on the drawings to their left. Do the same for the extensors on the right. (2) Color the supinators and pronators below. the arrows demonstrating their actions, and their attachment sites at upper left.

4 FLEXORS.
BICEPS BRACHII₄
BRACHIALISв
BRACHIORADIALISс
PRONATOR TERESᴅ

Medial epicondyle

The principal flexors of the elbow joint are *brachialis* and *biceps brachii*, of which the former has the best mechanical advantage. Yet it's the bulge of a contracted biceps that gets all the visual attention! The tendon of biceps inserts at the tuberosity of the radius, making the muscle a supinator of the forearm as well. With the limb supinated, the biceps works to fulfill flexion of the elbow and supination of the elbow. Take away the supinating function (flexing the pronated elbow), and the appearance of biceps is disappointing (in most of us!). Note the additional attachment of the bicipital aponeurosis into the deep fascia of the common flexor group (not shown) in the forearm. *Brachioradialis* is active in flexion of the elbow and in rapid extension where it counters the centrifugal force produced by that movement. *Pronator teres* assists in elbow flexion as well as pronation.

Long head
Short head
Bicipital aponeurosis (cut)
Radius
Ulna
Interosseous ligament
Styloid process

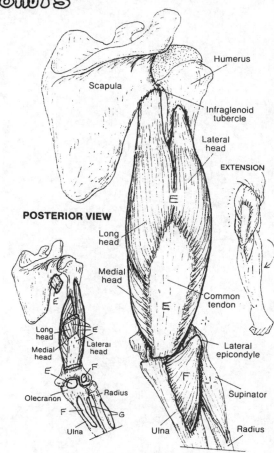

Scapula
Humerus
Infraglenoid tubercle
Lateral head
EXTENSION

POSTERIOR VIEW

Long head
Medial head
Common tendon
Lateral epicondyle
Supinator
Radius

Long head
Medial head
Lateral head
Olecranon
Radius
Ulna

2 EXTENSORS.
TRICEPS BRACHIIᴇ
ANCONEUSꜰ

The principal extensor of the elbow joint is the three-headed *triceps brachii* with its massive tendon of insertion. The smaller *anconeus* assists in this function. Triceps is a powerful antagonist to the elbow flexors.

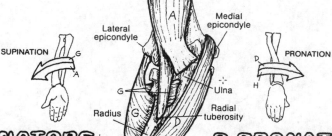

SUPINATION

Lateral epicondyle
Medial epicondyle
Ulna
Radial tuberosity
Radius

PRONATION

Interosseous ligament

2 SUPINATORS.
BICEPS BRACHIIₐ
SUPINATORɢ

Biceps brachii is the more powerful supinator of the elbow, but *supinator* is important in maintaining supination. Supinator arises from the lateral aspect of the elbow, passing obliquely downward and forward to a rather broad insertion on the upper lateral and anterior surface of the radius. A bundle of fibers from the upper lateral ulna passes behind the radius to join the lateral fibers of supinator.

2 PRONATORS.
PRONATOR TERESᴅ
PRONATOR QUADRATUSн

Pronator quadratus is the principal pronator of the elbow joint, superior in its mechanical advantage to *pronator teres*. Pronating the forearm (palm down) involves medial rotation of the radius. Since only the radius can rotate in the forearm, the pronators clearly cross the radius on the anterior side of the forearm, and their origin is ulnar.

ANTERIOR VIEW

MOVERS OF WRIST & HAND JOINTS

FLEXORS *¹

DEEP LAYER

FLEX. DIGITORUM PROFUNDUS ᴀ
FLEX. POLLICIS LONGUS ʙ

INTERMEDIATE LAYER

FLEX. DIGITORUM SUPERFICIALIS ᴄ

SUPERFICIAL LAYER

FLEX. CARPI ULNARIS ᴅ
PALMARIS LONGUS ᴇ
FLEX. CARPI RADIALIS ꜰ

CN: A more detailed view of the tendons of these muscles (with the same subscripts) can be seen among the intrinsic muscles of the hand on the next plate. (1) Begin with the flexors; note the deeper muscles have been omitted from the superficial view. Color gray the entire flexor mass in the smaller illustration. (2) Continue with the extensors, coloring gray the entire extensor mass in the smaller illustration.

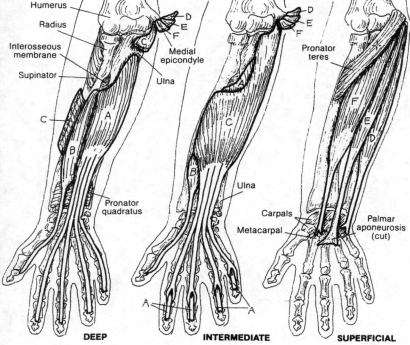

ANTERIOR VIEW

The flexors of the wrist (carpus) and fingers (digits) take up most of the anterior compartment of the forearm, arising as a group from the medial epicondyle, the upper radius and ulna, and the intervening interosseous membrane. The deep layer of muscles in the anterior forearm (*flexor pollicis longus* or FPL in the radial half, *flexor digitorum profundus* or FDP in the ulnar half) lie in contact with the radius and ulna. The superficial layer of muscles (wrist flexors: the *"carpi" muscles and palmaris longus*) is seen just under the skin and thin superficial fascia. The intermediate layer (*flexor digitorum superficialis*, FDP) lies between the superficial and deep groups. In the anterior (palmar) fingers, note how the tendons of FDS, which insert on the sides of the middle phalanges, split at the level of the proximal phalanges, permitting the deeper (posterior) tendons of FDP to pass on through to the bases of the distal phalanges.

DEEP   **INTERMEDIATE**   **SUPERFICIAL**

EXTENSORS *²

DEEP LAYER

EXT. INDICIS ɢ
EXT. POLLICIS LONGUS ʜ
EXT. POLLICIS BREVIS ɪ

SUPERFICIAL LAYER

EXT. CARPI ULNARIS ᴊ
EXT. DIGITI MINIMI ᴋ
EXT. DIGITORUM ʟ
EXT. CARPI RADIALIS LONGUS ᴍ
EXT. CARPI RADIALIS BREVIS ɴ

ABDUCTOR POLLICIS LONGUS ᴏ

The extensors of the wrist and fingers arise from the lateral epicondyle and upper parts of the bones and interosseous membrane of the forearm, forming an extensor compartment on the posterior side of the forearm. The wrist extensors insert on the distal carpal bones or metacarpals, while the finger extensors form an expansion of tendon over the middle and distal phalanges to which the small intrinsic muscles of the hand insert. The wrist extensor muscles are critical to hand function: grasp a finger of one hand with your fingers and an extended wrist of the other; now try it with wrist fully flexed. Note that the power of the hand exists only with an extended wrist.

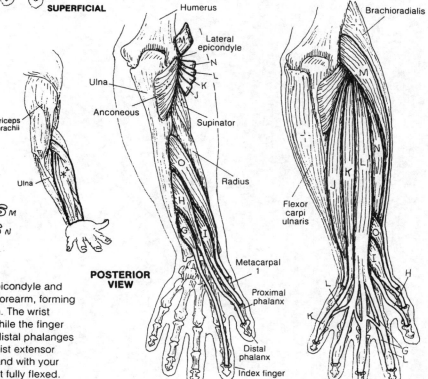

POSTERIOR VIEW

DEEP   **SUPERFICIAL**

MOVERS OF HAND JOINTS (INTRINSICS)

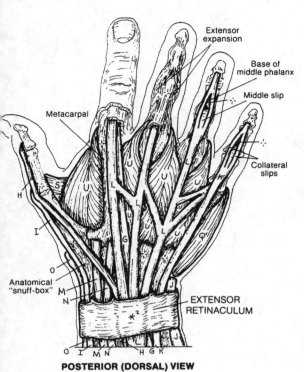

CN: The extrinsic muscles that move the wrist and finger joints were covered on Plate 58, and their tendons are shown in dark line and labeled here for identification and study, *but not for coloring.* If possible, use different colors on this plate. (1) Color the muscles of the two anterior views, as well as the flexor retinaculum (gray). (2) Color the posterior view. (3) In the illustration of finger abduction (at the bottom) note that the little finger is not moved by the dorsal interosseous (U).

Extensor expansion
Base of middle phalanx
Middle slip
Metacarpal
Collateral slips
H
I
O
Anatomical "snuff-box"
M
N
EXTENSOR RETINACULUM
O I M N L H G K

POSTERIOR (DORSAL) VIEW

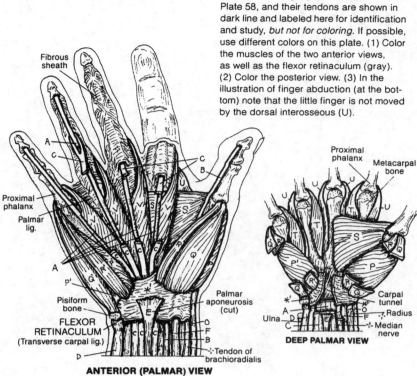

Fibrous sheath
Proximal phalanx
Palmar lig.
Pisiform bone
FLEXOR RETINACULUM (Transverse carpal lig.)
Palmar aponeurosis (cut)
Tendon of brachioradialis

ANTERIOR (PALMAR) VIEW

Proximal phalanx
Metacarpal bone
Carpal tunnel
Radius
Ulna
Median nerve

DEEP PALMAR VIEW

THENAR EMINENCE*'
OPPONENS POLLICIS_P
ABDUCTOR POLLICIS BREVIS_Q
FLEXOR POLLICIS BREVIS_R

Note the palpable bulge of muscle (thenar eminence) just proximal to the thumb on your own hand. Integrated with the action of the other thumb movers, these three muscles make possible complex movements of the thumb. The thenar muscles arise/insert in the same general area as one another; however, their different orientation orders different functions.

HYPOTHENAR EMINENCE*
OPPONENS DIGITI MINIMI_P'
ABDUCTOR DIGITI MINIMI_Q'
FLEXOR DIGITI MINIMI BREVIS_R'

These muscles move the 5th digit; they are complementary to the thenar muscles in attachment and function. The function of opposition is basic to some of the complex grasping functions of the hand.

DEEP MUSCLES
ADDUCTOR POLLICIS_S
PALMAR INTEROSSEUS_T
DORSAL INTEROSSEUS_U
LUMBRICAL_V

Adductor pollicis, in concert with the first dorsal interosseous muscle, provides great strength in grasping an object between thumb and index finger... try it. The *interossei* and *lumbrical muscles* insert into expanded finger extensor tendons (extensor expansion; see posterior view) forming a complex mechanism for flexing the metacarpophalangeal joints and extending the interphalangeal joints. By their phalangeal insertions, the interossei abduct/adduct certain digits.

ACTIONS OF INTRINSIC MUSCLES
ON THE THUMB*

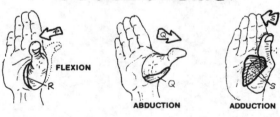

FLEXION

ABDUCTION

ADDUCTION

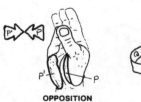

OPPOSITION

CIRCUMDUCTION

ON THE FINGERS

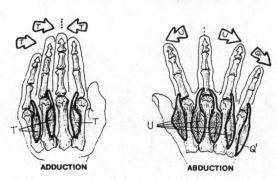

ADDUCTION

ABDUCTION

MUSCLES OF THE GLUTEAL REGION

CN: In the posterior and lateral views (superficial dissections), the upper fibers of the illiotibial tract (✗¹) have been cut away, exposing gluteus medius. (1) Color each muscle in all views, including the directional arrows, before going on to the next. The origin of piriformis (E) cannot be seen in these views, but see Plate 52. A better view of the origin of obturator internus (F) also can be seen on Plate 52.

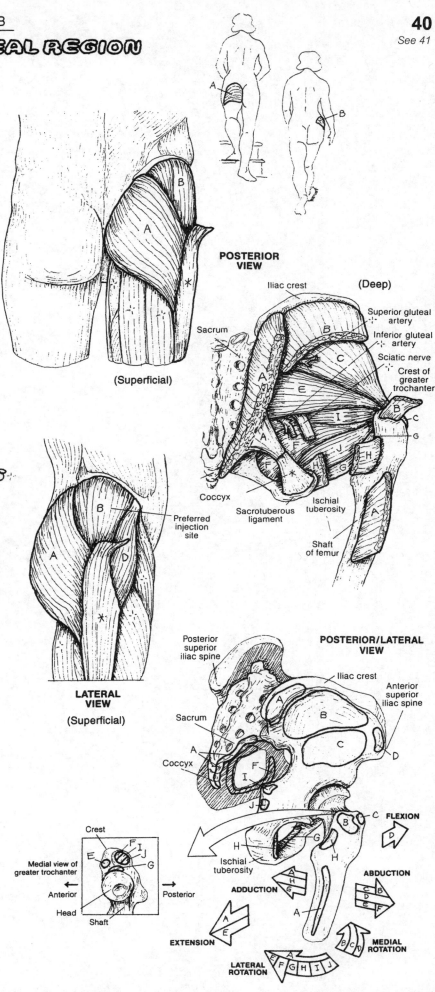

2 GLUTEAL MUSCLES:

GLUTEUS MAXIMUS_A
GLUTEUS MEDIUS_B
GLUTEUS MINIMUS_C
TENSOR FASCIAE LATAE_D

The gluteal muscles are arranged in three layers: the most superficial is *gluteus maximus*. The large sciatic nerve runs deep to it, as every student nurse has learned well. Its thickness varies. Gluteus maximus extends the hip joint during running and walking uphill, but does not act in relaxed walking. The intermediately placed, more lateral *gluteus medius* is a major abductor of the hip joint and an important stabilizer (leveler) of the pelvis when the opposite lower limb is lifted off the ground.

6 DEEP, LATERAL ROTATORS:

PIRIFORMIS_E
OBTURATOR INTERNUS_F
OBTURATOR EXTERNUS_G
QUADRATUS FEMORIS_H
GEMELLUS SUPERIOR_I
GEMELLUS INFERIOR_J

The deepest layer of gluteal muscles is the *gluteus minimus* and the *lateral rotators* of the hip joint. They cover up/fill the greater and lesser sciatic notches. These muscles generally insert at the posterior aspect of the greater trochanter of the femur. The gluteal muscles (less gluteus maximus) correspond to some degree with the rotator cuff of the shoulder joint: lateral rotators posteriorly, abductor (gluteus medius) superiorly, medial rotators (gluteus medius and minimus, tensor fasciae latae) anteriorly.

ILIOTIBIAL TRACT*

The iliotibial tract, a thickening of the deep fascia (fascia lata) of the thigh, runs from ilium to tibia and helps stabilize the knee joint laterally. The muscle *tensor fasciae latae*, a frequently visible and palpable flexor and medial rotator of the hip joint, inserts into this fibrous band, tensing it. Despite its major flexor function, this anterolaterally-placed muscle is considered a part of the more posterior gluteal group; it shares its insertion into the iliotibial tract with gluteus maximus, and it is supplied by the superior gluteal nerve and artery.

MUSCLES OF THE POSTERIOR THIGH

HAMSTRINGS∗
SEMIMEMBRANOSUS ᴀ
SEMITENDINOSUS ʙ
BICEPS FEMORIS ᴄ

CN: (1) Color each hamstring muscle in the deep view before going on to the superficial. Then color the diagrams of flexion and extension. (2) Color gray the outline of the muscles in the drawings at upper right.

Tight hamstrings limit flexion of hip when knee joint is extended.

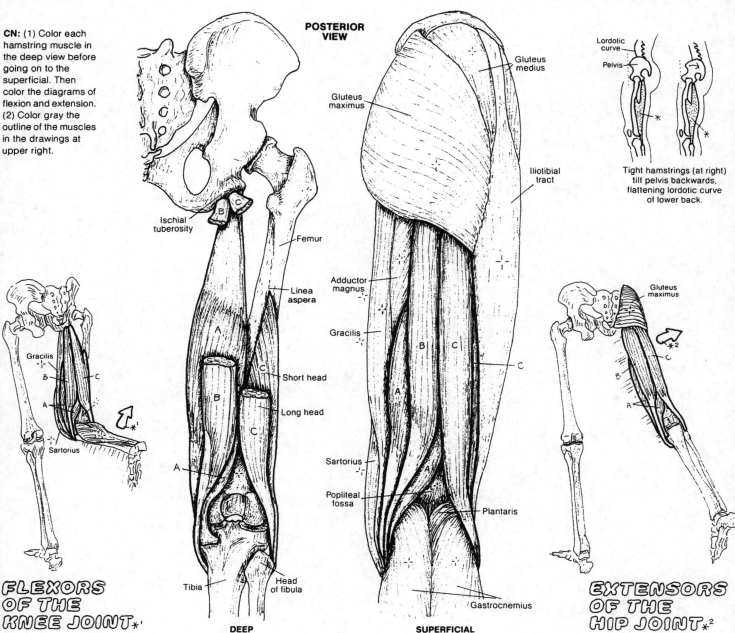

POSTERIOR VIEW

Gluteus medius

Gluteus maximus

Iliotibial tract

Ischial tuberosity

Femur

Linea aspera

Adductor magnus

Gracilis

Short head

Long head

Sartorius

Popliteal fossa

Plantaris

Gracilis

B

C

A

Sartorius

Tibia

Head of fibula

Gastrocnemius

Lordotic curve

Pelvis

Tight hamstrings (at right) tilt pelvis backwards, flattening lordotic curve of lower back.

Gluteus maximus

FLEXORS OF THE KNEE JOINT ∗¹

DEEP

SUPERFICIAL

EXTENSORS OF THE HIP JOINT ∗²

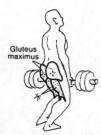

Gluteus maximus

Powerful extensors of the hip joints.

The hamstring muscles are equally effective at both extension of the hip joint and flexion of the knee joint. Unlike the hip extensor gluteus maximus, the hamstrings are active during normal walking. In relaxed standing, both gluteus maximus and the hamstrings are inactive. In knee flexion, the hamstrings act in concert with sartorius, gracilis, and gastrocnemius (Plates 63 and 66). Long tendons of the hamstrings can be palpated just above the partially flexed knee on either side of the midline.

Reduced hamstring stretch ("tight hamstrings") limits hip flexion with the knee extended; flexion of the knee permits increased hip flexion. Try this on yourself. Tight hamstrings, by their ischial origin, pull the posterior pelvis down, lengthening the erector spinae muscles and flattening the lumbar lordosis, potentially contributing to limitation of lumbar movement and back pain. Tight hamstrings often cause posterior thigh pain on straight leg raise testing (subject is supine, lower limbs horizontal; one heel is lifted, progressively flexing the hip joint with knee extended). This pain from muscle stretch may be confused with sciatic nerve/nerve root pain, which normally shoots into the leg and foot.

MUSCLES OF THE FOOT (INTRINSICS)

CN: Feel free to use the colors used for the letter labels on plates 65 and 66. Those letters are presented here for identification, and the muscles they refer to are not meant to be colored. Also note that plantar surface attachment sites for those extrinsic foot muscles have been omitted in the illustration of the fourth layer but can be found on the two preceding plates. (1) Begin with the fourth layer and complete each illustration before going on to the next.

The dorsal intrinsic muscles of the foot (those that arise and insert within the dorsum of the foot) are limited to two *small extensors* of the toes, shown at right, most of the extensor function being derived from extrinsic extensors.

The intrinsic muscles of the plantar region of the foot are shown here in four layers. The *plantar interossei*, wedged between the metatarsal bones, constitute the deepest (4th) layer. They adduct toes 3–5, flex the metatarsophalangeal (MP) joints of these toes, and contribute to extension of the interphalangeal (IP) joints of these toes through the mechanism of the extensor expansion. The *dorsal interossei* abduct toes 3–5 and facilitate the other actions of the plantar interossei.

The third layer of muscles acts on the great toe (hallux) and 5th digit (digiti minimi). The second layer includes the *quadratus plantae*, inserting into the lateral border of the common tendon (H) of flexor digitorum longus (FDL). It assists that muscle in flexion of the toes. The *lumbricals* arise from the individual tendons of FDL and insert into the medial aspect of the extensor expansion (dorsal aspect). They flex the MP joints and extend the IP joints of toes 2–5 via the extensor expansion.

The superficial (first) layer consists of the *abductors* of the 1st and 5th digits and the *flexor digitorum brevis*. The plantar muscles are covered by the thickened deep fascia of the sole, the plantar aponeurosis, extending from calcaneus to the fibrous sheath of the flexor tendons.

DORSAL SURFACE (Right foot)

EXTENSOR DIGITORUM BREVIS N

EXTENSOR HALLUCIS BREVIS O

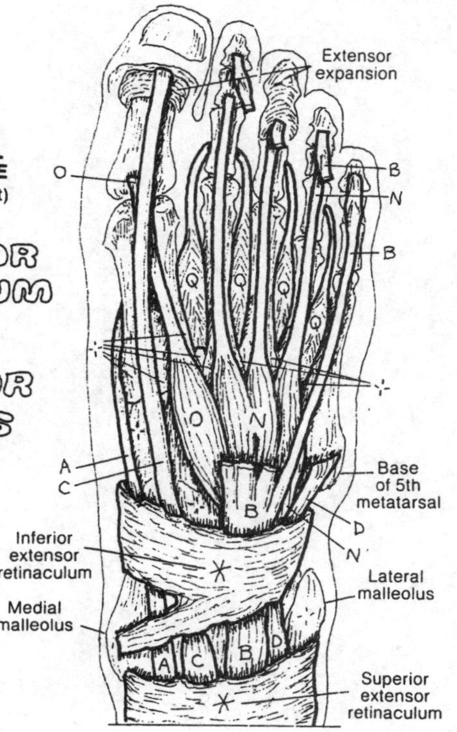
Extensor expansion
O
B
N
B
Q
A
C
Base of 5th metatarsal
D
N'
Inferior extensor retinaculum
Lateral malleolus
Medial malleolus
Superior extensor retinaculum

FLEX. HALLUCIS BREVIS R

ADDUCTOR HALLUCIS S

FLEX. DIGITI MINIMI BREV. T

ABDUCTOR HALLUCIS W

ABDUCTOR DIGITI MINIMI X

FLEX. DIGITOR. BREVIS Y

3 PLANTAR INTEROSSEI P

4 DORSAL INTEROSSEI Q

QUADRATUS PLANTAE U

4 LUMBRICALS V

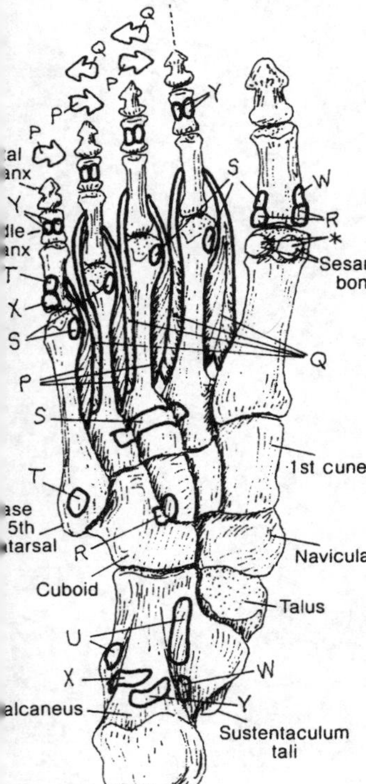
Q
P
Y
W
S
R
Sesamoid bones
T
X
S
P
Q
1st cuneiform
Navicular
Cuboid
Talus
U
X
W
Y
Sustentaculum tali

FOURTH LAYER

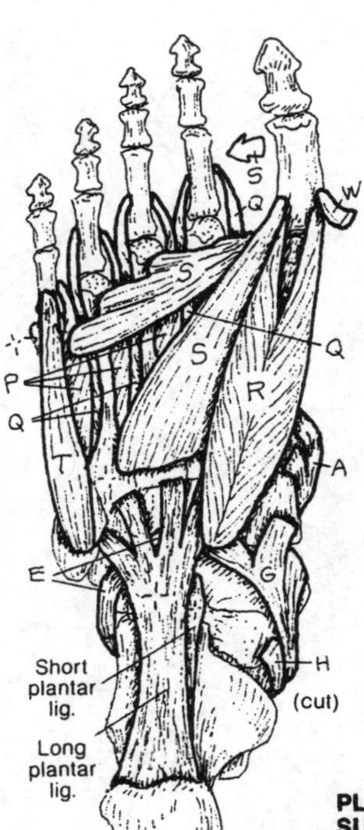
S
Q
W
S
Q
P
Q
S
R
T
A
E
G
H
(cut)
Short plantar lig.
Long plantar lig.

THIRD LAYER

PLANTAR SURFACE (Right foot)

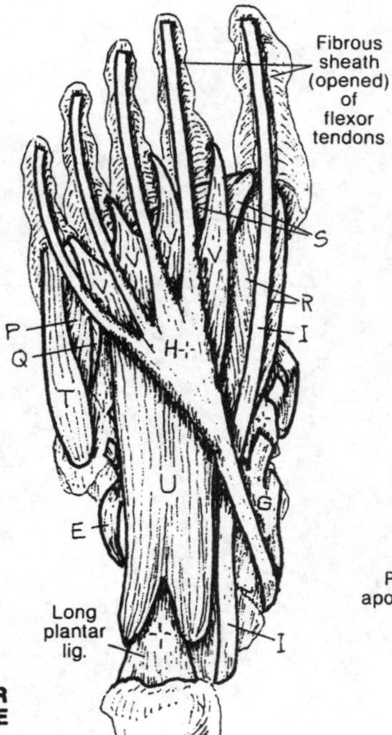
Fibrous sheath (opened) of flexor tendons
S
V
R
I
P
Q
H
T
U
G
E
Long plantar lig.
I

SECOND LAYER

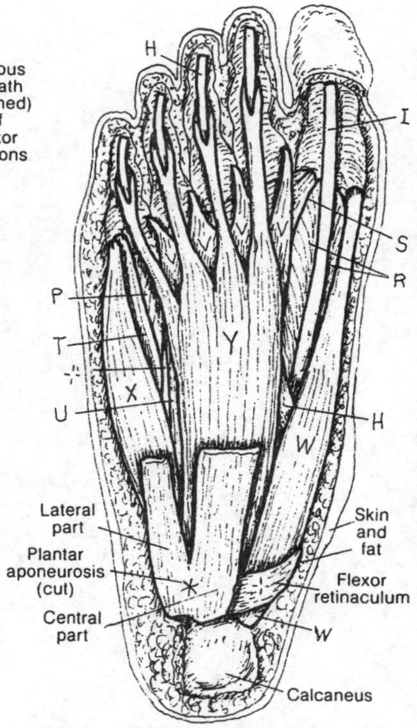
H
I
S
R
P
Y
T
X
U
H
W
Lateral part
Skin and fat
Plantar aponeurosis (cut)
Flexor retinaculum
Central part
W
Calcaneus

FIRST LAYER (superficial)

ORGANIZATION

CN: Use very light colors for A and C. The numbers in parentheses following the titles under Spinal Nerves refer to the number of nerves in each of the regions listed. (1) In the central illustration, the spinal cord has been brought out of the vertebral column to show its regions in relation to the vertebrae. Spinal nerves, depicting regional limits, are shown with arrowheads pointing to the same spinal nerves emerging from the vertebral column. Avoid coloring the filum terminale—it is not a spinal nerve. (2) At upper right, color the cranial nerves. (3) At lower right, color over the lines representing the spinal nerves and their branches on the left side of the figure. Color the autonomic ganglia on the right side of the spinal cord.

CENTRAL NERVOUS SYSTEM (CNS):

BRAIN:
CEREBRUM A
BRAINSTEM B
CEREBELLUM C

SPINAL CORD D
REGIONS D−
CERV. D G THOR. D H LUM. D I SAC. D J CO. K

The nervous system consists of neurons arranged into a highly integrated central part (central nervous system, or CNS) and bundles of neuronal processes (nerves) and islands of neurons (ganglia) largely outside the CNS making up the peripheral part (peripheral nervous system, or PNS). These neurons are supported by neuroglial cells and a rich blood supply. Neurons of the CNS are interconnected to form centers (nuclei; gray matter) and axon bundles (tracts; white matter). The brain is the center of sensory awareness and movement, emotions, rational thought and behavior, foresight and planning, memory, speech, and language and interpretation of language.

The spinal cord, an extension of the brain and part of the CNS, begins at the foramen magnum of the skull, traffics in ascending/descending impulses, and is a center for spinal reflexes, source of motor commands for muscles below the head, and receiver of sensory input below the head.

PERIPHERAL NERVOUS SYSTEM (PNS):

CRANIAL NERVES (12 PAIR) E
SPINAL NERVES & BRANCHES F
CERVICAL (8) G'
THORACIC (12) H'
LUMBAR (5) I'
SACRAL (5) J'
COCCYGEAL (1) K'

AUTONOMIC NERVOUS SYS.:
SYMPATHETIC DIV. L
PARASYMPATHETIC DIV. M

The PNS consists largely of bundles of sensory and motor axons (nerves) radiating from the brain (*cranial nerves*) and spinal cord (*spinal nerves*) segmentally and bilaterally and reaching to all parts of the body (visceral and somatic) through a classic pattern of distribution. *Branches* of spinal nerves are often called peripheral nerves. Nerves conduct all sensations from the body to the brain and spinal cord; they conduct motor commands to all the skeletal muscles of the body. The *autonomic nervous system* (ANS) is a subset of ganglia and nerves in the PNS dedicated to visceral movement and glandular secretion and to the conduction of visceral sensations to the spinal cord and brain.

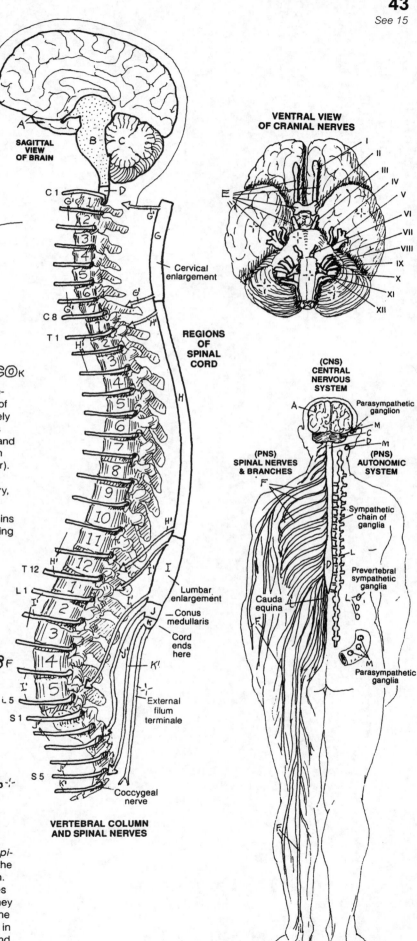

SAGITTAL VIEW OF BRAIN

Cervical enlargement

REGIONS OF SPINAL CORD

Lumbar enlargement

Conus medullaris

Cord ends here

External filum terminale

Coccygeal nerve

VERTEBRAL COLUMN AND SPINAL NERVES

VENTRAL VIEW OF CRANIAL NERVES

I, II, III, IV, V, VI, VII, VIII, IX, X, XI, XII

(CNS) CENTRAL NERVOUS SYSTEM

Parasympathetic ganglion

(PNS) SPINAL NERVES & BRANCHES

(PNS) AUTONOMIC SYSTEM

Sympathetic chain of ganglia

Prevertebral sympathetic ganglia

Cauda equina

Parasympathetic ganglia

FUNCTIONAL CLASSIFICATION OF NEURONS

CN: Use light colors throughout the plate. Do not color the summary diagram at the top of the page until completing the rest of the plate.

Neurons generally function in one of three modes: They conduct impulses from receptors in the body to the central nervous system or CNS (sensory or afferent neurons); they conduct motor command impulses from the CNS to muscles of the body (motor or efferent neurons); or they form a network of interconnecting neurons in the CNS between motor and sensory neurons (interneurons). If the sensory or motor neurons relate to musculo-skeletal structures or the skin and fascia, the prefix "somatic" may be applied (somatic afferent/somatic efferent). If these neurons are related to organs with hollow cavities (viscera), the prefix "visceral" may be applied (visceral afferent/visceral efferent).

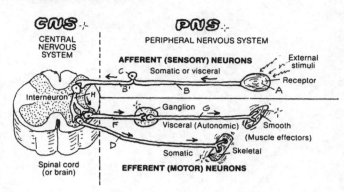

PNS:
SENSORY NEURON
RECEPTOR A
AXON
(PERIPHERAL PROCESS) B
CELL BODY C
AXON
(CENTRAL PROCESS) B'

Sensory neurons conduct impulses from sensory *receptors* to synapses in the CNS. The receptors may be sensitive to touch, pressure, pain, joint position, muscle tension, chemical concentration, light, or other mechanical stimulus, basically providing information on the external or internal environment and related changes. Sensory neurons are unipolar neurons, with certain exceptions (bipolar neurons), and are characterized by *peripheral processes* ("axons"), *cell bodies*, and *central processes* ("axons").

PNS:
SOMATIC MOTOR N.
DENDRITE D
CELL BODY C'
AXON
MOTOR END PLATE E

Motor neurons conduct impulses from *cell bodies* located in the CNS through *axons* that leave the CNS and subsequently divide into branches, each of which becomes incorporated into the cell membrane of a muscle cell (*motor end plate*). Here the neuron releases its neurotransmitter, which induces the muscle cell to shorten.

PNS:
AUTONOMIC MOTOR N.
PREGANGLIONIC NEURON F
POSTGANGLIONIC NEURON G

Autonomic motor neurons function as paired units connected at a ganglion by a synapse. The first or *preganglionic neuron* arises in the CNS, and its axon embarks for a ganglion located some distance from the CNS. There it *synapses* with the cell body or dendrite of a *postganglionic neuron* whose axon proceeds to the effector organ: smooth muscle, cardiac muscle, or glands.

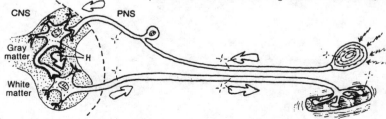

CNS:
INTERNEURON
(ASSOCIATION N.) H

Interneurons are found mostly in the CNS. They make up the bulk of the neurons of the brain and spinal cord. They come in a variety of shapes and sizes. Many of them are directly related to incoming (sensory) impulses and others to outgoing motor commands. Others serve to integrate sensory or ascending input with higher centers to effect an appropriate motor output.

SYNAPSES & NEUROTRANSMITTERS

CN: Use light colors for A, B, and C. (1) In the upper drawing, each of the synapses shown has two parts. Color only the ones labeled with subscripts (A, B. C). Color the nerve impulse title (D, at the top) and the related directional arrows. (2) Color the numbered steps in the lower drawing. Note the change of color in the presynaptic membrane between exocytosis (H) and endocytosis (K).

BASIC TYPES OF SYNAPSES:

AXO·A AXONIC·A
AXO·A SOMATIC·B
AXO·A DENDRITIC·C

Connections between and among neurons are called synapses. The great majority are non-contact connections in which chemical neurotransmitters carry the impulse from one neuron to another. Electrical synapses (where electrically charged atoms or ions pass from one neuron to another by way of protein channels; not shown) also exist in the brain and embryonic nervous tissue but are far less common. Most synapses are *axodendritic*; that is, the axon of one neuron synapses with the dendrite or dendritic spine of another neuron. The neuron in front of the synapse is said to be presynaptic. The second neuron is said to be postsynaptic. Another common synapse is *axosomatic*, where the axon of one neuron and the cell body (soma) of another neuron communicate by way of neurotransmitters. Other, more infrequently seen synapses are illustrated here as well. For example, note the complex of synapses (a glomerulus) between three axons and a dendritic spine, all surrounded by a neuroglial sheath.

Synapses permit the conduction of electrochemical impulses among myriad neurons almost instantly. Synapses vary from simple reflex arcs (see Plate 85) to polysynaptic pathways in the brain and spinal cord that involve millions of synapses. A single motor neuron of the spinal cord may have as many as 10,000 synapses on its body and dendrites! Multiple synapses greatly increase the available options of nervous activity. The ability to integrate, coordinate, associate, and modify sensory input and memory to achieve a desired motor command is directly related to the number of synapses in the pathway.

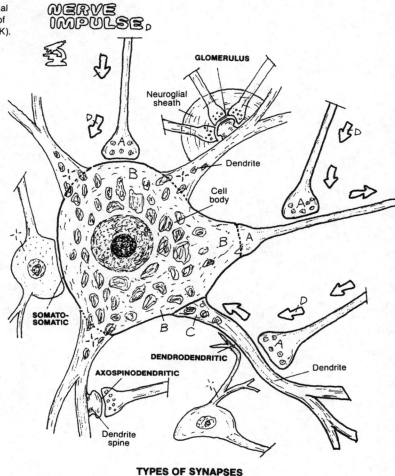

TYPES OF SYNAPSES

TYPICAL SYNAPSE:

PRESYNAPTIC AXON·A
PRESYNAPTIC MEMBRANE·E
SYNAPTIC VESICLE·F
NEUROTRANSMITTER·G
FRAGMENT·G'
EXOCYTOSIS·H
SYNAPTIC CLEFT·I
POSTSYNAPTIC MEMBRANE·J
RECEPTOR·G'
ENDOCYTOSIS·K

Here we show a typical axodendritic synapse. (1) The *presynaptic axon* transmits the electrochemical impulse toward the synapse. As the impulse reaches the axon terminal, calcium ion (Ca^{++}) channels/gates are opened in the cell membrane, and extracellular Ca^{++} pours into the axon terminal. (2) *Synaptic vesicles*, loaded with *neurotransmitter* (e.g., acetylcholine, norepinephrine), influenced by the incoming Ca^{++}, migrate toward the *presynaptic membrane* and fuse with it (3). Following fusion, neurotransmitter is spilled from the vesicles into the tiny synaptic cleft (*exocytosis*). Neurotransmitter molecules bind to receptor proteins on the *postsynaptic membrane* of the dendrite; ion channels are opened, and the altered membrane potential (impulse) is propagated along the dendrite (4). Inactivated neurotransmitter *fragments* are taken up by the presynaptic membrane (5; *endocytosis*), enclosed in a synaptic vesicle, and resynthesized (6).

The electrical activity of the postsynaptic membrane may be facilitated or inhibited by the neurotransmitter. If sufficiently excited by multiple facilitory synapses, the postsynaptic neuron will depolarize and transmit an impulse to the next neuron or effector (muscle cell, gland cell). Sufficiently depressed by multiple inhibitory synapses, the neuron will not depolarize and will not transmit an impulse.

**ELECTROCHEMICAL TRANSMISSION
AT THE SYNAPSE**

CEREBRAL HEMISPHERES

CN: Use light colors for B, E, I, and J. (1) Color the coronal section; most of the frontal lobe and part of the temporal lobe have been removed. Color the cerebral cortex (A) gray. In the two large hemispheres the stippled areas of specialized function are parts of lobes, but receive their own colors. Color the arrows identifying the major fissures and sulcus. (3) Color gray the diagram illustrating how the convolutions provide increased surface area in a smaller space.

CEREBRAL CORTEX (GRAY MATTER)A∗

FRONTAL LOBEB
PRINCIPAL SPEECH AREAC
PRIMARY MOTOR AREA (PRECENTRAL GYRUS)D
PARIETAL LOBEE
PRIMARY SENSORY AREA (POSTCENTRAL GYRUS)F
TEMPORAL LOBEG
AUDITORY AREAH
OCCIPITAL LOBEI
VISUAL AREAJ

MAJOR FISSURES/SULCUS ∴
LONGITUDINAL FISSUREK
CENTRAL SULCUSL
LATERAL FISSUREM

SUBCORTICAL WHITE MATTERN∴

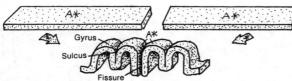

CORTICAL CONVOLUTIONS: INCREASED SURFACE AREA

The paired cerebral hemispheres (cerebrum), derivatives of the embryonic telencephalon (see Plate 169), consist of four major elements: (1) an outer cerebral cortex of gray matter, the topography of which reveals fissures (deep grooves), gyri (hills), and sulci (furrows); (2) underlying white matter consisting of numerous tracts destined for or leaving the cortex and oriented along three general directions (Plate 74); (3) discrete masses of gray matter at the base of the cerebrum (basal nuclei) that subserve motor areas of the cortex (Plate 74); (4) paired cavities called lateral ventricles (Plate 80). The cerebral cortex is the most highly evolved area of the brain. About 2–4 mm (roughly 1/6 inch) thick, the cortex is divided into lobes distinctly bordered by sulci; the lobes are generally related to the cranial bones that cover them: frontal, parietal, temporal, occipital. The exception is the limbic lobe (part of which is shown); it incorporates parts of other (frontal, temporal, parietal) lobes.

Cortical mapping experiments (based on electrical stimulation and clinical/pathologic data) have been the principal methods by which functions of the cortex have been discovered. All parts of the cortex are concerned with storage of experience (memory), exchange of impulses with other cortical areas (association), and the two-way transmission of impulses with subcortical areas (afferent/efferent projections).

The frontal lobe is concerned with intellectual functions such as reasoning and abstract thinking, aggression, sexual behavior, olfaction (smell), articulation of meaningful sound (*speech*), and voluntary movement (*precentral gyrus*). The *central sulcus* separates the frontal lobe from the parietal lobe. The *parietal lobe* is concerned with body sensory awareness, including taste (*postcentral gyrus*), the use of symbols for communication (language), abstract reasoning (e.g., mathematics), and body imaging. The *temporal lobe* is partly limbic and here is concerned with the formation of emotions (love, anger, aggression, compulsion, sexual behavior); the non-limbic portion of the temporal lobe is concerned with interpretation of language and awareness and discrimination of sound (hearing; *auditory area*); it constitutes a major memory processing area. The *occipital lobe* is concerned with receiving, interpreting, and discriminating visual stimuli from the optic tract and associating those visual impulses with other cortical areas (e.g., memory).

The limbic lobe or system is the oldest part of the cortex, in evolutionary terms. It is the center of emotional behavior. The limbic neurons occupy parts of the inferior and medial cortices of each hemisphere, and some subcortical areas as well. Certain limbic areas are closely related topographically to the olfactory tracts.

The cerebral hemispheres appear structurally as mirror images of one another; functionally they are not. The speech area develops fully only on one side, usually the left. In general, the left hemisphere tends to deal with certain higher functions (mathematical, analytical, verbal) while the right concentrates on visual, spatial, and musical orientations. The matter of cerebral "dominance" (left hemisphere, left speech center, righthandedness, or vice versa) is quite controversial.

TRACTS/NUCLEI OF CEREBRAL HEMISPHERES

CN: Use very light colors for F and G. (1) Color gray the various sections of cerebral cortex without coloring the cortical surfaces.

CEREBRAL CORTEX A*
SUBCORTICAL AREAS ⫶
BASAL NUCLEI ⫶
CAUDATE NUCLEUS B
LENTICULAR NUCLEUS C
LATERAL VENTRICLE D
WHITE MATTER TRACTS ⫶
COMMISSURES E
CORPUS CALLOSUM E'
PROJECTION TRACTS F
CORONA RADIATA F'
INTERNAL CAPSULE F²
ASSOCIATION TRACTS G

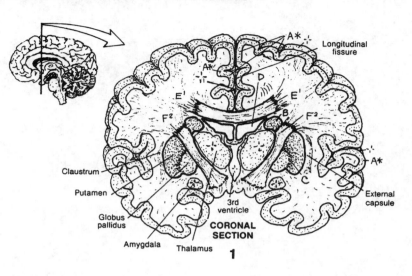

1

CORONAL SECTION

Claustrum
Putamen
Globus pallidus
Amygdala
Thalamus
3rd ventricle
External capsule
Longitudinal fissure

Below the cerebral cortex, the cerebral hemispheres embody centrally placed cavities, masses of gray matter at the base of the cerebrum, and bundles of white matter. These structures can be colored in the coronal section at upper right cerebrum (1).

The basal nuclei are discrete, bilateral islands of gray matter on either side of and above the diencephalon (Plate75). They consist primarily of the tail-shaped *caudate nucleus* and the lens-shaped *lenticular nucleus* (2). These structures can be colored in illustrations 1, 2, 3, and 4. The lenticular nucleus is further divided into the medial globus pallidus and the more lateral putamen (1). Each of these nuclei is part of the extrapyramidal system (Plate 79). They have extensive connections among themselves, with the cerebral cortex, and with nuclei of the diencephalon. They are concerned with the maintenance of muscle tone and the programming of subconscious, sequential postural adjustments. They monitor and mediate descending motor commands from the cerebral cortex.

The subcortical white matter of the hemispheres is arranged into bundles or bands (tracts) of largely myelinated axons essentially arranged in three axes (5). They conduct impulses among various areas of the cortex. The largest commissure is the *corpus-callosum*, forming a roof over the subcortical nuclei (1). It is bent caudally at both anterior and posterior ends (genu and splenium) (4, 6). Association tracts connect anterior and posterior cerebral cortices (5). They exist as both short and long tracts (6).

The most spectacular tract is the fan-shaped array of fibers called the *corona radiata* (5, 7). This projection system radiates caudally from all areas of the cortex. It narrows into a curved band (internal capsule; 1, 2, 3, 4) as it descends between the caudate nucleus and the thalamus medially, and the putamen laterally. The term "internal capsule" refers to the inner wall of the figurative encapsulation of the basal nuclei (1, note external capsule). The axons of the projection tract continue through the diencephalon into the brain stem and spinal cord; many make connections en route (Plates 78, 79).

2 SUBCORTICAL AREAS (Anteriolateral view)

Thalamus
Amygdala
Head
Tail

3
Right hemisphere
Left hemisphere
Putamen

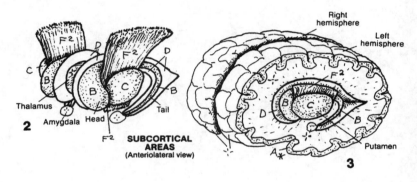

4 HORIZONTAL SECTION

RIGHT HEMISPHERE
Splenium
Genu
Anterior
Third ventricle
Thalamus
Insula
LEFT HEMISPHERE

5 TRACT DIRECTIONS (Superior view)

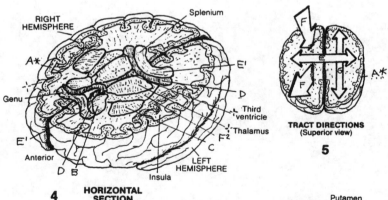

7 MEDIAL VIEW (Right hemisphere section)

Anterior
Putamen

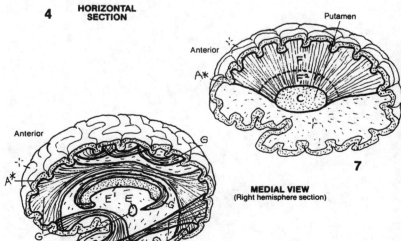

6
Anterior
Anterior commissure

DIENCEPHALON

CN: Use light colors for A and B, and a very bright color for C. (1) Color each structure wherever it appears before going on to the next title. (2) Although not colored, the neighboring relations of the diencephalic structures are important and have been identified by name. These should be given special attention.

DIENCEPHALON÷
THALAMUS A
HYPOTHALAMUS B
EPITHALAMUS
(PINEAL GLAND) C
THIRD VENTRICLE D

The diencephalon, the smaller of two derivatives of the early forebrain, fits between but is not part of the surrounding cerebral hemispheres (see drawings 2 and 3). It consists largely of paired masses of nuclei and related tracts of white matter arranged around the thin, purse-like third (III) ventricle (2 and 3). The nature of this cavity can be seen in Plate 80.

On each side of the third ventricle, note the *thalamus*, *subthalamus*, and *hypothalamus* (2 and 3). The *epithalamus* or *pineal gland* is a midline structure seeming to hang off the posterior thalamus. The relationship of these nuclei to the basal nuclei and internal capsule should be carefully studied while coloring to ensure orientation (recall Plate 74).

The thalamus (1–4) consists of several groups of cell bodies and processes that, in part, process all incoming impulses from sensory pathways (except olfactory). It has broad connections with the motor, general sensory, visual, auditory, and association cortices. Not surprisingly, the corticothalamic (cortex to thalamus) fibers contribute significantly to the *corona radiata*. Still other thalamic nuclei connect to the *hypothalamus* and other brainstem nuclei. Thalamic activity (1) integrates sensory experiences resulting in appropriate motor responses, (2) integrates specific sensory input with emotional (motor) responses (e.g., a baby crying in response to hunger), and (3) regulates and maintains the conscious state (awareness), subject to facilitating/inhibiting influences from the cortex. *Subthalamic nuclei* (3) are concerned with motor activity and have connections with the basal ganglia.

The hypothalamus (1, 3, and 4) consists of nuclear masses and associated tracts on either side of the lower third ventricle. The hypothalamus maintains neuronal connections with the frontal and temporal cortices, thalamus, neurohypophysis, and brainstem. Its neurosecretions (hormones) are also directed to the *adenohypophysis* via the hypophyseal portal system. In addition, the hypothalamus is concerned with emotional behavior, regulation of the autonomic (visceral) nervous system and related integration of visceral (autonomic) reflexes with emotional reactions, and activation of the drive to eat (hunger) and the subsequent feeling of satisfaction (satiety) following fulfillment of that drive. Finally, it mediates descending impulses related to both reflexive and skilled movement—all of this in an area the size of four peas!

The epithalamus (pineal gland) (1) consists primarily of the pineal body and related nuclei and tracts that have connections with the thalamus, hypothalamus, basal nuclei, and the medial temporal cortex. It produces melatonin (a pigment-enhancing hormone), the synthesis of which is related to diurnal cycles or rhythms (body activity in day or sunlight as opposed to dark or nocturnal periods). It may influence the onset of puberty through inhibition of testicular/ovarian function. Remarkably, the pineal is the only unpaired structure in the brain.

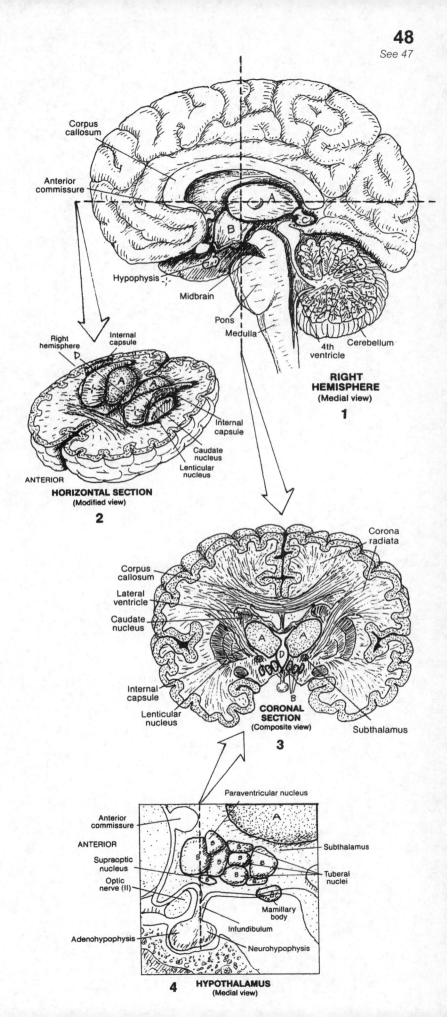

Corpus callosum

Anterior commissure

Hypophysis

Midbrain

Pons

Medulla

4th ventricle

Cerebellum

RIGHT HEMISPHERE
(Medial view)
1

Right hemisphere

Internal capsule

Internal capsule

Caudate nucleus

Lenticular nucleus

ANTERIOR

HORIZONTAL SECTION
(Modified view)
2

Corona radiata

Corpus callosum

Lateral ventricle

Caudate nucleus

Internal capsule

Lenticular nucleus

CORONAL SECTION
(Composite view)
3

Subthalamus

Paraventricular nucleus

Anterior commissure

ANTERIOR

Supraoptic nucleus

Optic nerve (II)

Adenohypophysis

Subthalamus

Tuberal nuclei

Mamillary body

Infundibulum

Neurohypophysis

4 **HYPOTHALAMUS**
(Medial view)

BRAIN STEM/CEREBELLUM

CN: Use darker colors for C, E, and M and the lightest for K. (1) As you color each structure in as many views as it is shown, take particular note of the orientation of the view. (2) Note that the fourth ventricle is located in both parts of the hindbrain and receives the same color in both parts. The diencephalon has been presented on the previous plate and is shown here only for orientation.

BRAIN STEM

DIENCEPHALON A
MIDBRAIN B
CEREBRAL AQUEDUCT C
SUPERIOR COLLICULUS B'
INFERIOR COLLICULUS B²
CEREBRAL PEDUNCLE F
SUP. CEREBELLAR PEDUNCLE D

HINDBRAIN
4TH VENTRICLE E
PONS F
MID. CEREBELL. PED. G
MEDULLA OBLONGATA H
INF. CEREBELL. PED. I

The brain stem includes the diencephalon, midbrain, pons, and medulla oblongata. Throughout the brain stem, the brain cavity (Plates 80, 82) takes on different shapes, a reflection of the kind of differential growth the brain underwent during development (Plate 169). The cerebellum is attached to the brain stem (by peduncles) but is not considered a part of the brain stem. See Plate 75 for information on the diencephalon.

In the midbrain, the *cerebral peduncles* are composed of long descending tracts that originate in the cerebral cortex, descend through the internal capsule (recall Plate 74), and continue caudally to the pons and medulla (for cranial nerves) and the spinal cord (for spinal nerves). Immediately posterior to these tracts in the midbrain is the tegmentum, an area of neurons associated with the reticular formation and cranial nerves III and IV, and multiple tracts. The superior cerebellar peduncles transmit fibers to the *cerebellum* from the spinal cord, and fibers to the thalamus and medulla from the cerebellum. The superior colliculi are centers for visual reflexes; the inferior colliculi make possible auditory reflexes (e.g., rapid, involuntary movements in response to visual and auditory stimuli).

The pons is characterized by its massive anterior bulge consisting of stalks of white matter that bridge the 4th ventricle (pons = bridge) to reach the cerebellum as the middle cerebellar peduncles. These fibers largely arise from neurons in the pons—neurons that convey impulses from both motor and sensory areas of the cerebral cortex. Cranial nerve nuclei V, VI, VII, and VIII are located here. Both ascending and descending tracts pass through here, including the neurons of the reticular formation.

The medulla contains life-sustaining control centers of respiration, heart rate, and vasomotor function. Nuclei for cranial nerves VIII, IX, X, XI, and XII exist here. The inferior cerebellar peduncles carry fibers to the cerebellum from the spinal cord and brain stem vestibular and reticular systems, as well as fibers from the cerebellum to the vestibular system.

CEREBELLUM J
ARBOR VITAE K
CEREBELLAR CORTEX L*
DEEP CEREB. NUCLEUS M

The cerebellum consists of two hemispheres, with a cortex of gray matter on its surface (*cerebellar cortex*), central masses of motor-related (*deep cerebellar*) nuclei, and bands of white matter forming a treelike appearance (*arbor vitae* = tree of life) when the cerebellum is cut in section. The cerebellum is attached to the brain stem by the three cerebellar peduncles. The cerebellum is concerned with equilibrium and position sense, fine movement, control of muscle tone, and overall coordination of muscular activity in response to proprioceptive input and descending traffic from higher centers.

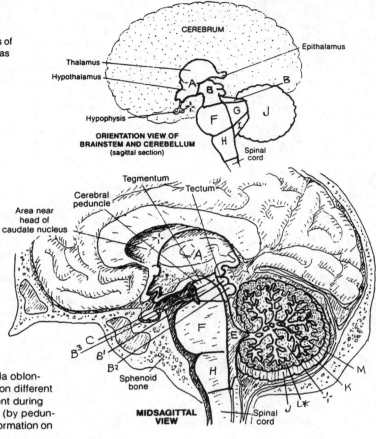

CEREBRUM

Epithalamus

Thalamus

Hypothalamus

Hypophysis

ORIENTATION VIEW OF BRAINSTEM AND CEREBELLUM (sagittal section)

Spinal cord

Tegmentum

Cerebral peduncle

Tectum

Area near head of caudate nucleus

Sphenoid bone

Spinal cord

MIDSAGITTAL VIEW

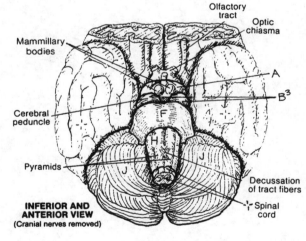

Olfactory tract

Optic chiasma

Mammillary bodies

Cerebral peduncle

Pyramids

A

B³

Decussation of tract fibers

Spinal cord

INFERIOR AND ANTERIOR VIEW (Cranial nerves removed)

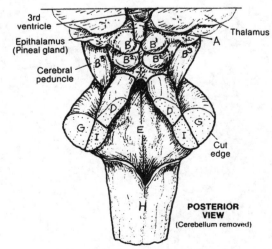

3rd ventricle

Epithalamus (Pineal gland)

Cerebral peduncle

Thalamus

Cut edge

POSTERIOR VIEW (Cerebellum removed)

SPINAL CORD

CN: Use bright colors for A–C (except where indicated by asterisk (∗) or no-color symbol (-⸫-). Use gray for D∗, medium dark colors for E–I, and light colors for K–M. (1) In the upper drawing, color B∗ gray over the nerve roots within the dura mater and outside the spinal cord. (2) Color the cord sections taken at various levels. (3) Color the meninges of the spinal cord. What is not shown (due to space limitations) is the presence of the arachnoid and subarachnoid space (and cerebrospinal fluid) around the nerve roots. (4) Do not color the structures within the subarachnoid space or the central canal in the drawing at the bottom of the plate.

SPINAL CORD ₐ
MENINGES -⸫-
PIA MATER ₐ'
INTERNAL FILUM TERMINALE ₐ²
SUBARACHNOID SPACE ₆∗
ARACHNOID ₆'
DURA MATER ᴄ
EXTERNAL FILUM TERMINALE ᴄ'
EPIDURAL SPACE ᴄ⁺⸫-

The spinal cord is the lower extension of the central nervous system. It takes off from the medulla oblongata at the foramen magnum of the skull and ends as the *conus medullaris* at the vertebral level of L1 or L2. It bulges slightly in the lower cervical and lumbar segments where it gives off the roots of spinal nerves destined for the upper and lower limbs, respectively. The cord is ensheathed by *three coverings (meninges)*: the thin, vascular *pia mater* closely applied to the spinal cord, the translucent *arachnoid* separated from the pia by the subarachnoid space, and the tough, fibrous *dura mater* that is a prolongation of the dura surrounding the brain.

The pia forms triangular sheets that project away from the cord between the pairs of nerve roots. These sheets extend to the dura and are called *denticulate ligaments*. The pia extends below the conus medullaris as the thin cord-like *filum terminale internum*, ending at the dural sac at the vertebral level of S2. The subarachnoid space is filled with *cerebrospinal fluid (CSF)*; the space ends inferiorly as the dural sac; its CSF-containing cavity is the lumbar cistern. Outside the dura is the *epidural space*, containing fat and veins.

GRAY MATTER ᴅ∗
POSTERIOR HORN ₑ
ANTERIOR HORN ꜰ
LATERAL HORN (T1-L2) ɢ
INTERMEDIATE ZONE ₕ
GRAY COMMISSURE ᵢ

WHITE MATTER ⱼ-⸫-
POSTERIOR FUNICULUS ₖ
LATERAL FUNICULUS ₗ
ANTERIOR FUNICULUS ₘ

The spinal cord consists of a central mass of gray matter arranged into the form of an H and a peripheral array of white matter *(funiculi)* consisting of descending and ascending tracts. The amount of white matter decreases as the cord progresses distally, seen especially well in the sacro-coccygeal region. The gray *posterior horns* (actually columns when seen in three dimensions) receive the central processes of sensory neurons (recall Plate 71) and direct incoming impulses to the adjacent white matter for conduction to other cord levels or higher centers. The *anterior horns* include lower motor neurons that represent the "final common pathway" for motor commands to muscle. *Lateral horns* exist only in the thoracic and upper lumbar cord and include autonomic motor neurons supplying smooth muscle (in vessels and viscera) and glands. It is in the gray matter that spinal reflexes occur in conjunction with facilitory and inhibitory influences from higher centers.

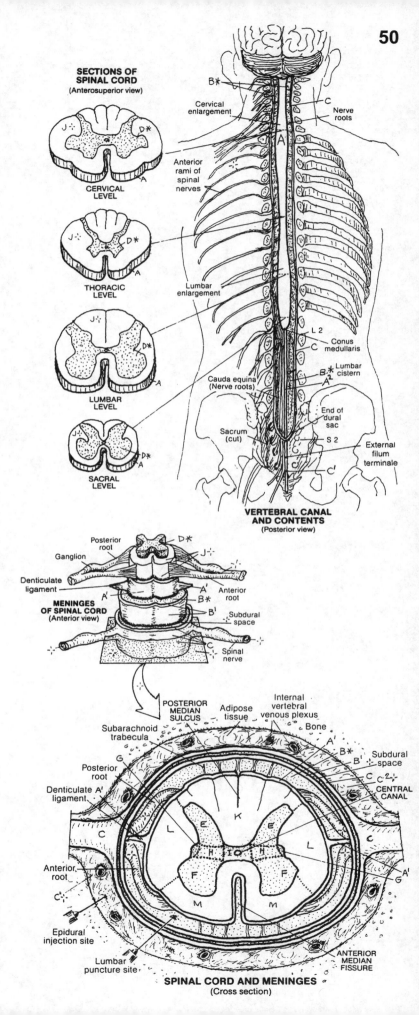

SECTIONS OF SPINAL CORD
(Anterosuperior view)

CERVICAL LEVEL

THORACIC LEVEL

LUMBAR LEVEL

SACRAL LEVEL

Cervical enlargement
Nerve roots
Anterior rami of spinal nerves
Lumbar enlargement
L 2
Conus medullaris
Lumbar cistern
Cauda equina (Nerve roots)
Sacrum (cut)
End of dural sac
S 2
External filum terminale

VERTEBRAL CANAL AND CONTENTS
(Posterior view)

Posterior root
Ganglion
Denticulate ligament
Anterior root
Subdural space
Spinal nerve

MENINGES OF SPINAL CORD
(Anterior view)

POSTERIOR MEDIAN SULCUS
Subarachnoid trabecula
Posterior root
Denticulate ligament
Anterior root
Epidural injection site
Lumbar puncture site
Adipose tissue
Internal vertebral venous plexus
Bone
Subdural space
CENTRAL CANAL
ANTERIOR MEDIAN FISSURE

SPINAL CORD AND MENINGES
(Cross section)

ASCENDING TRACTS

CN: Use bright colors for A–C and a light color for F. (1) Color the pain/temperature pathway, which is shown on one side only for visual simplicity. Note that the sensory cortex and the thalamus are to be colored gray. (2) In the muscle stretch/position sense pathways, note there are two different cerebellar peduncles, each receiving a different color.

Ascending pathways consist of linearly arranged neurons, the axons of which travel in a common bundle (tract) conducting impulses toward the thalamus, cerebral cortex, or cerebellum. In the examples shown here, each of the pathways begins with a sensory neuron. These sensory pathways permit body surface sensations and muscle/tendon stretch information (below the head) to reach brain stem and cerebellar centers for response and cortical centers for awareness.

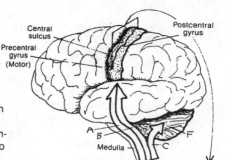

PAIN/TEMPERATURE A

SENSORY NEURON A'
LAT. SPINOTHALAMIC TRACT A²
THALAMUS *'
THALAMOCORTICAL TRACT A³
SENSORY CORTEX *²

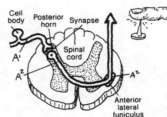

Pain and temperature receptors on the body surface and elsewhere below the head generate impulses that travel to the spinal cord by axons of *sensory neurons* (1st-order neuron). The central process ("axon") of each sensory neuron enters the posterior horn and synapses with the 2nd-order neuron whose axon crosses (decussates) to the contralateral side, enters the lateral funiculus, and ascends as part of the *lateral spinothalamic tract*. This neuron ascends to the thalamus, where it synapses with relay (3rd-order) neurons, the axons of which traverse the internal capsule and corona radiata (*thalamocortical tract*) to reach the postcentral gyrus of the cerebral cortex ("sensory cortex").

TOUCH/PRESSURE B

SENSORY NEURON B'
N. CUNEATUS & GRACILIS B²
INT. ARCUATE FIBERS B³
MED. LEMNISCUS B⁴
THALAMUS *'
THALAMOCORTICAL TRACT B⁵
SENSORY CORTEX *²

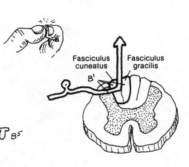

Touch and pressure receptors below the head generate electrochemical impulses that travel to the spinal cord through *sensory neurons* that enter the posterior horn and join/ascend the posterior funiculus (posterior columns) to the medulla. Here they synapse with 2nd-order neurons in the *nuclei cuneatus* and *gracilis*. The axons of these neurons sweep to the opposite side (as *internal arcuate fibers*) to form an ascending bundle (*medial lemniscus*) in the brain stem that terminates in the thalamus. There these axons synapse with 3rd-order relay neurons whose axons reach the postcentral gyrus of the cerebral cortex via the *thalamocortical tract.*

MUSCLE STRETCH/POSITION SENSE C

SENSORY NEURON C'
POST. SPINOCEREBELLAR TRACT C²
INF. CEREBELLAR PED. D
ANT. SPINOCEREBELLAR TR. C³
SUP. CEREBELLAR PED. E
CEREBELLAR CORTEX F

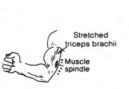

Impulses from muscle spindles and other proprioceptors (receptors responsive to muscle stretch/loads) are conducted by *sensory neurons* to the spinal cord. Single receptor input is conducted by 2nd-order neurons that ascend the ipsilateral lateral funiculus (*posterior spinocerebellar tract*) and enter the cerebellum via the *inferior cerebellar peduncle.* More global proprioceptive input ascends the contralateral anterior *spinocerebellar tract* and enters the cerebellum via the *superior cerebellar peduncle.* By these and similar pathways that function in the absence of awareness, the cerebellum maintains an ongoing assessment of body position, muscle tension, muscle overuse, and movement. In turn, it mediates descending impulses from cortical and subcortical centers destined for motor neurons.

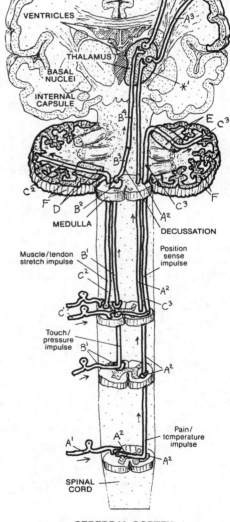

CEREBRAL CORTEX, CEREBELLUM, AND SPINAL CORD

(Schematic)

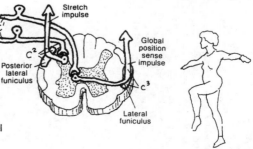

DESCENDING TRACTS

CN: Use light colors for H, I, and K. (1) Color the pyramidal tract in the sagittal view. (2) Color the pyramidal tract in the schematic coronal section at upper right, including the percentage figures. (3) Color the extra-pyramidal system.

PYRAMIDAL TRACT / RELATED AREAS :-
MOTOR CORTEX *
CORTICOSPINAL TRACT A'
LAT. A² / ANT. CORTICOSPINAL TRACT A³
MEDULLARY PYRAMID A⁴
LATERAL FUNICULUS B
ANTERIOR FUNICULUS C
FINAL COMMON PATHWAY :-
LOWER MOTOR NEURON D
EFFECTOR E

The principal neural pathway for voluntary movement is the *corticospinal tract*. Its neuronal cell bodies are in the pre-central gyrus of each frontal lobe (motor cortex). The axons of these neurons descend—without synapse—through the corona radiata, internal capsule, cerebral peduncles, pons, and medulla into the spinal cord. Pathways are often named according to their origin and their termination, and in that order; hence, cortico- (referring to cortex) spinal (referring to the spinal cord). The corticospinal tracts form bulges, called pyramids, on the anterior surface of the medulla, hence the name "*pyramidal tract*." Eighty percent of these tracts cross (decussate) to the contralateral side in the medulla (*decussation of the pyramids*); 20% do not. In the spinal cord, many corticospinal fibers terminate on inter-neurons (recall Plate 71) at the base of the posterior horn (not shown); the majority end by synapsing with anterior horn motor neurons. Corticospinal input to the lower motor (anterior horn) neurons, however, is only one input for desired skeletal muscle function.

EXTRAPYRAMIDAL SYSTEM :-
PONTINE RETICULOSPINAL TRACT F
VESTIBULOSPINAL TRACT G
INTERNEURON H

Each lower motor neuron receives axons from multiple descending tracts, many of which conduct impulses related to body position, memory, and a host of other commands necessary for any given movement at any given time. These collective inputs from the cerebral cortex, basal nuclei, cerebellum, and elsewhere arrive at the appropriate lower motor neurons by a number of descending pathways, none of which pass through the medullary pyramids (hence, extrapyramidal system or tracts). Two major extrapyramidal tracts are shown here: the *reticulospinal tract* from the brain stem reticular nuclei and the *vestibulospinal tract* from the vestibular nuclei in the brain stem. Other tracts include the rubrospinal and tectospinal tracts (not shown, but see glossary). The synaptic connections of these axons with each lower motor neuron (often by way of *interneurons*) are in the thousands. Depending on the neurotransmitter produced by the presynaptic neuron, the synapse may facilitate or inhibit production of an excitatory impulse from the lower motor neuron. Discharge of the lower motor neuron, or lack of it, is dependent on the sum of the facilitory and inhibitory impulses impinging on it at any moment. Once generated, the electrochemical impulse moving down the axon of the lower motor neuron reaches the effector without further mediation. Thus, the anterior horn motor neuron is truly the final common pathway for the ultimate expression of all nervous activity: muscular contraction.

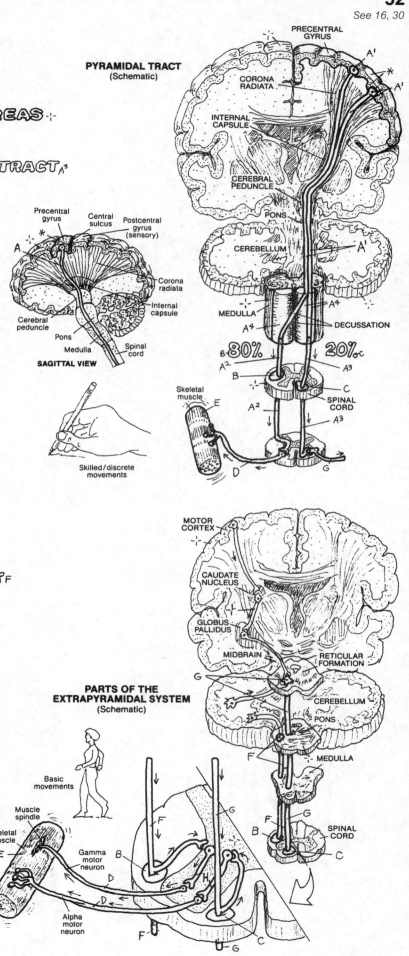

PYRAMIDAL TRACT (Schematic)

PRECENTRAL GYRUS
CORONA RADIATA
INTERNAL CAPSULE
CEREBRAL PEDUNCLE
PONS
CEREBELLUM
MEDULLA
DECUSSATION
B **80%** 20% C
SKELETAL MUSCLE
SPINAL CORD

Precentral gyrus
Central sulcus
Postcentral gyrus (sensory)
Corona radiata
Internal capsule
Cerebral peduncle
Pons
Medulla
Spinal cord
SAGITTAL VIEW

Skilled / discrete movements

MOTOR CORTEX
CAUDATE NUCLEUS
GLOBUS PALLIDUS
MIDBRAIN
RETICULAR FORMATION
CEREBELLUM
PONS
MEDULLA
SPINAL CORD

PARTS OF THE EXTRAPYRAMIDAL SYSTEM (Schematic)

Basic movements
Muscle spindle
Skeletal muscle
Gamma motor neuron
Alpha motor neuron

CRANIAL NERVES

53
See 43

CN: Use light colors throughout. (1) Beginning with the first cranial nerve, color the title on the left; the large Roman numeral, the cranial nerve (cut), and the related function arrow at lower left; and the Roman numeral and accompanying illustration at upper right. The illustrations generally depict target organs/areas. (2) Note carefully the direction of the function arrows at lower left (sensory/afferent is incoming; motor/efferent is outgoing). (3) The accessory nerve (XI) has two roots: a spinal root and a cranial root that travels with the vagus nerve (X).

CRANIAL NERVES∗

OLFACTORY (O)₁

OPTIC (OO)ıı

OCULOMOTOR (OOO)ııı

TROCHLEAR (OV)ıv

TRIGEMINAL (V)v

ABDUCENS (VO)vı

FACIAL (VOO)vıı

VESTIBULOCOCHLEAR (VOOO)vııı

GLOSSOPHARYNGEAL (OX)ıx

VAGUS (X)x

ACCESSORY (XO)xı

HYPOGLOSSAL (XOO)xıı

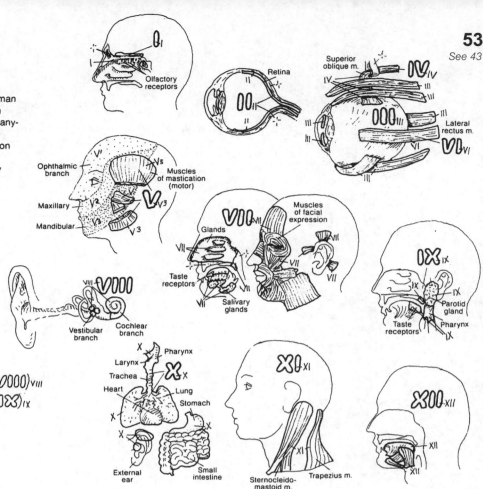

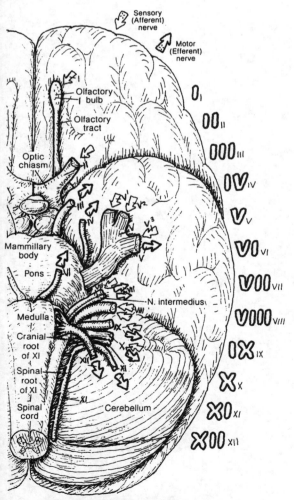

ANTERIOR-INFERIOR SURFACE
(Left brain, brainstem, and cerebellum)

Cranial nerves I and II are derived from the forebrain; all others arise from the brain stem. *V* = *visceral*, referring to smooth muscle, glands, and organs with hollow cavities; *S* = *somatic*, referring to the skin, eye, skeletal, facial, and skeletal muscles; *A* = *afferent or sensory*; *E* = *efferent or motor.* All motor nerves depicted include proprioceptive fibers (sensory for muscle, tendon, and joint movement).

I   VA: smell-sensitive (olfactory) receptors in roof/walls of nasal cavity.

II   SA: light-sensitive (visual) receptors in the retina of the eye.

III   SE: to extrinsic eye muscles (exc. lat. rectus and sup. oblique); VE: parasympathetic to ciliary and pupillary sphincter (eye) muscles via ciliary ganglion in the orbit.

IV   SE: to superior oblique muscle of the eye.

V   SA: from face via three divisions indicated; VE: to muscles of mastication, tensor tympani, tensor veli palatini, mylohyoid, and digastric muscles.

VI   SE: to lateral rectus muscle of the eye.

VII VA: from taste receptors ant. tongue; SA: from ext. ear; VE parasympathetic to glands of nasal/oral cavity, lacrimal gland (via pterygopalatine ganglion in fossa of same name), submandibular/sublingual salivary glands (via submandibular ganglion in region of same name); VE: to facial muscles, stapedius (mid. ear), stylohyoid, post. digastric muscles.

VIII SA: cochlear part is sound-sensitive; vestibular part is sensitive to head balance and movement (equilibrium).

IX   VA: from taste receptors post. one-third tongue; SA: from ext. ear and ext. auditory canal; VA: from mucous membranes of posterior mouth, pharynx, auditory tube, and middle ear; from pressure and chemical receptors in carotid body and common carotid artery; VE: to sup. constrictor m. of the pharynx, stylopharyngeus; VE: parasymp. to parotid gland (via otic ganglion in infratemporal fossa).

X   VA: from taste receptors at base of tongue and epiglottis; SA: from ext. ear and ext. aud. canal; VA: from pharynx, larynx, thoracic and abdominal viscera; VE: to muscles of palate, pharynx, and larynx; VE: parasymp. to muscles of thoracic and abdominal viscera (via intramural ganglia).

XI   Cranial root: joins vagus (VA to laryngeal muscles); spinal root (C1–C5): innervates trapezius and sternocleidomastoid muscles.

XII   SE: to extrinsic and intrinsic muscles of tongue.

SPINAL NERVES & NERVE ROOTS

CN: Use very light colors for D through G. (1) Begin with the upper illustration. Color all three pairs of spinal nerves as they emerge from the intervertebral foramina (M). (2) Color the cross-sectional view in the center. (3) Color the spinal nerve axons and the arrows representing direction of impulse flow.

SPINAL NERVE ROOT

POSTERIOR ROOT A
SENSORY AXON B
CELL BODY C
POSTERIOR ROOT GANGLION D
ANTERIOR ROOT E
MOTOR AXON F
CELL BODY G

SPINAL NERVE H   RAMUS H'

Spinal nerves are collections of axons of sensory and motor neurons located in or adjacent to the spinal cord. They are the spinal equivalent of cranial nerves. Spinal nerves arise from nerve roots that come directly off the spinal cord. The spinal nerves and their roots are arranged segmentally (from cervical to coccygeal) and bilaterally along the length of the spinal cord. The central relations of these spinal nerves/roots can be recalled in Plates 78 and 79. The spinal nerves branch soon after they are formed into *anterior and posterior rami*.

Axons of sensory neurons that form the major part of the *posterior root* are called central processes (see drawing of spinal nerve axons). The cell bodies of these neurons form the posterior root ganglia and are located in or near the intervertebral foramina, except for the sacral and coccygeal nerves, whose ganglia are in the vertebral canal. The peripheral processes of the sensory neurons join with the *axons of motor neurons* to form the spinal nerves.

The cell bodies of the motor neurons are multipolar and exist in the anterior horns of the spinal cord. Their axons emerge from the cord to form the anterior roots of the spinal nerves.

The nerve roots join to form the spinal nerves in the region of the *intervertebral foramina*. The nerve roots are progressively longer from cervical to coccygeal regions because the spinal cord does not fill the vertebral canal; it ends at the level of the 1st lumbar vertebra. Thus, some spinal nerve roots are quite long, remaining within the vertebral canal before reaching the lumbar, sacral, and coccygeal intervertebral foramina. The collection of these long nerve roots forms the "cauda equina" (recall Plate 77).

NERVE ROOT RELATIONS

VERTEBRA
BODY I
LAMINA J
ARTICULAR PROCESS K
VERTEBRAL CANAL L
LATERAL RECESS L'
INTERVERTEBRAL FORAMEN M

Spinal nerves and their roots have fairly tight quarters. The relations of these nerves and roots can best be appreciated in the cross-sectional view. Nerve roots are vulnerable to irritation (radiculitis) from encroaching, hypertrophic bone in the lateral recesses (degenerative joint disease), from bulging intervertebral discs (degenerative disc disease), or from cysts, meningeal tumors, and so on. With compression of axons or blood vessels supplying the axons, functional deficits can result (radiculopathy: sensory loss, motor loss, and/or tendon reflex change).

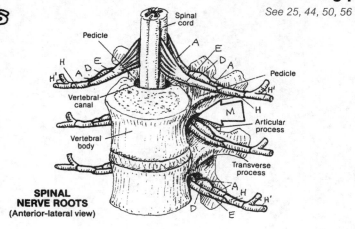

SPINAL NERVE ROOTS
(Anterior-lateral view)

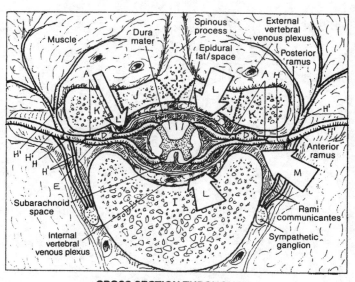

CROSS SECTION THROUGH T9
(Seen from above)

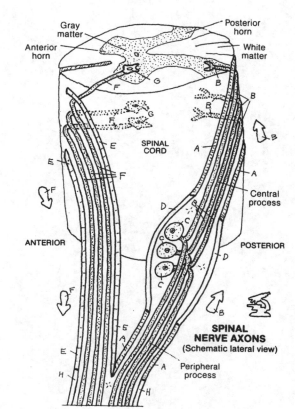

SPINAL NERVE AXONS
(Schematic lateral view)

SPINAL REFLEXES

CN: Use light colors for A and C, and use the same colors you used on Pl. 84 for structures D–F. (1) Color the upper two illustrations simultaneously, in numerical sequence 1–6, including the arrows. The small arrows at the end of the muscle segments indicate contraction or stretch. (2) Color the lower two illustrations similarly. Note that the motor neuron synapsing with the inhibitory interneuron, and the related effector, are not colored.

MONOSYNAPTIC REFLEX

STRETCH RECEPTOR (N-T ORGAN)ₐ

STRETCH RECEPTOR (MUSCLE SPINDLE)ₐ'

SENSORY NEURONₐ²

SPINAL CORD_B

MOTOR NEURON_C

END PLATE_C'

EFFECTOR MUSCLE_D

SPINAL NERVES / ROOTS

SPINAL NERVE_E

BRANCH_E'

POSTERIOR ROOT_F

GANGLION_F'

ANTERIOR ROOT_G

A reflex is an involuntary muscle response to a stimulus. It is a fundamental activity of the nervous system; most body movements and movement of viscera are reflexive— e.g., heart rate, respiratory rate, peristalsis of gastrointestinal motion. Spinal reflexes involve sensory receptors, sensory neurons, interneurons of the spinal cord, motor neurons, and effectors.

The simplest spinal reflex is a monosynaptic reflex involving two neurons and one synapse (myotatic [stretch] or deep tendon reflex). The reflex is activated by stretching the tendon of a specific muscle, such as the tendon of quadriceps femoris at the knee. This can be done with the sharp tap of a small mallet used for such purposes (or with the 5th-digit side of a hand). The *receptors* responsive to such a stretch are the neurotendinous organs in the patellar ligament and the muscle spindle in the belly of the quadriceps muscle. Muscle spindles are encapsulated, specialized muscle fibers within muscle bellies that have nerve endings sensitive to muscle stretch. Impulses generated in these receptors (1) are conducted by *sensory neurons* (2) to the *spinal cord* (3); these synapse in the gray matter with the anterior horn *motor neurons* (4). The motor neuron conducts impulses to the *end plates* of the *effector* muscle (5). The muscle contracts sufficiently, in the case of the knee reflex ("jerk"), to extend the knee joint momentarily (6).

POLYSYNAPTIC REFLEX

PAIN RECEPTORₐ³

SENSORY NEURONₐ²

INTERNEURON_H

FACILITATORY (+)_H'

INHIBITORY (−)_H²

(+) MOTOR NEURON_C /EFFECTOR_D

(−) MOTOR NEURON_C' /EFFECTOR_D'

Polysynaptic reflexes range from simple withdrawal reflexes to complex reflexes involving several segments of the spinal cord and brain. The complexity of a polysynaptic reflex relies on the number of interneurons in the reflex and the number of synaptic contacts. In this case, temperature and pain receptors respond to a sharp increase in heat; sensory neurons conduct the impulse to the spinal cord. An interneuron receives the impulse. Branches of the interneuron excite two interneurons, one facilitatory and one inhibitory. The excitatory interneuron facilitates the firing of the motor neuron that induces the extensor muscle to contract, lifting the fingers from the flame. Simultaneously, the inhibitory neuron depresses the firing of the 2nd motor neuron (C3), and the antagonist flexor muscle is stretched without contracting, permitting the fingers to be withdrawn from the flame.

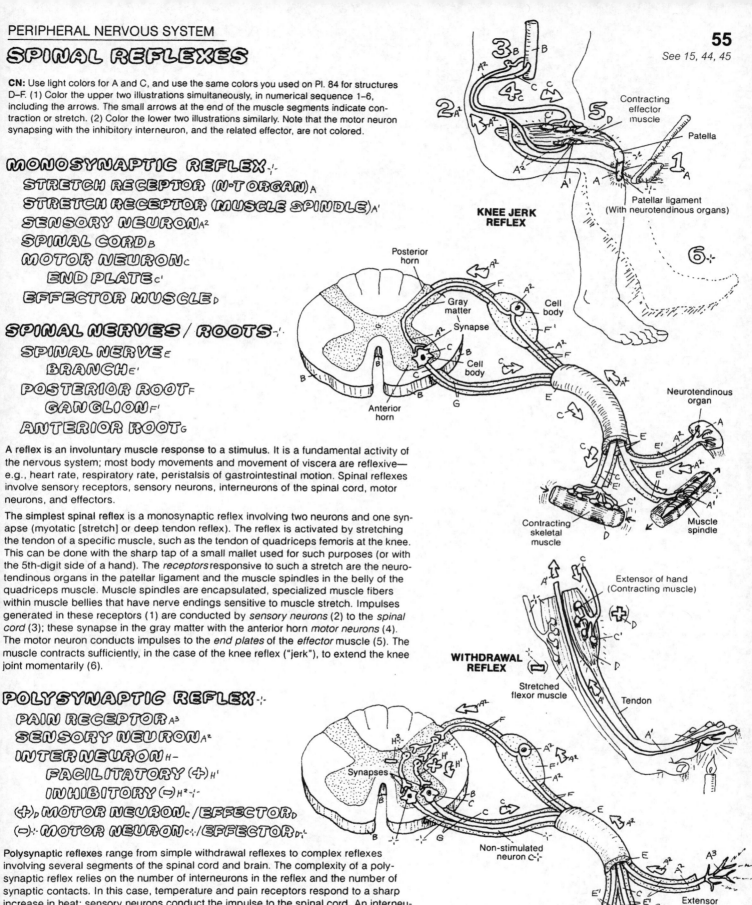

KNEE JERK REFLEX

Contracting effector muscle

Patella

Patellar ligament (With neurotendinous organs)

Posterior horn

Gray matter

Synapse

Cell body

Cell body

Anterior horn

Neurotendinous organ

Contracting skeletal muscle

Muscle spindle

WITHDRAWAL REFLEX

Extensor of hand (Contracting muscle)

Stretched flexor muscle

Tendon

Synapses

Non-stimulated neuron C

Flexor muscle

Extensor muscle

DISTRIBUTION OF SPINAL NERVES & THORACIC SPINAL NERVE

CN: (1) Begin with the upper illustration, which is an introduction to the major nerve plexuses (detailed on the following three plates) formed by spinal nerves. Note that each nerve (shown emerging from the left half of the spinal cord) receives the color of the plexus to which it contributes; exceptions are nerves T1 and L4, which make two contributions but receive the color of their main grouping. Thoracic nerves (C) give rise to intercostal nerves (O), represented above in the company of each rib and treated in more detail below. (2) Color the example of nerve coverings, taken from a cutaneous nerve (F¹) in the cross-sectional view to the right. (3) Color the larger view and review the introduction to these structures on Plate 84.

Thirty-one pairs of spinal nerves supply the body structure with sensory and motor innervation, except for areas covered by cranial nerves. From above to below, there are 8 cervical spinal nerves (C1–C8), 12 thoracic (T1–T12), 5 lumbar (L1–L5), 5 sacral (S1–S5), and one coccygeal (Co1). There is one more nerve than vertebrae in the cervical spine; C1 passes above the C1 vertebra, C8 passes below the C7 vertebra. Thus, spinal nerves after C6 pass below the vertebra of the same number; above C7 they pass above the vertebra of the same number.

Spinal nerves arise from roots; once formed, they split into rami (see Plate 84 and the cross section below right). The anterior rami of all spinal nerves (except thoracic) form interconnecting networks or plexuses outside the vertebral column. The posterior rami do not contribute to plexuses. Peripheral nerves are branchings from the plexuses and are directed to geographically related parts of the body. The nerves of the cervical plexus (C1–C4) can be colored in Plate 87, the nerves of the brachial plexus (C5–T1) in Plate 88, and the nerves of the lumbar plexus (L1–L4) and sacral plexus (S1–S4) in Plate 89. The coccygeal plexus (S4, S5, Co1) is not shown.

The anterior rami of thoracic spinal nerves form intercostal nerves, not plexuses (see Plate 50), although T1 contributes a branch to the brachial plexus. An idealized cross section through the thorax reveals the ring-like distribution of a "typical" thoracic spinal nerve (see below right). The anterior ramus of one thoracic nerve supplies a segment of the cutaneous, subcutaneous, and musculoskeletal areas of the torso, and the smaller posterior ramus (along with posterior rami of cervical and lumbar spinal nerves) supplies its posterior wall and that of the neck. Note the formation of the cutaneous branches to appreciate the innervation of the skin around the body (see also Plate 90).

A cross section through any nerve reveals coverings similar to those of muscle (Plate 44). These fibrous envelopes ensure physical security for the individual axons (endoneurium), fascicles of neurons (perineurium), and the entire nerve (epineurium continuous with deep fascia). These coverings also physically secure the vessels (vasa vasorum) and nerves (vasa nervosum) supplying the axons.

Spinal nerves and nerve plexuses (Posterior view)

Spinal cord (left half)
Spinal column (right half)
C1 spinal n.
C1 vertebra (cut)
8 cervical spinal nerves
C4 spinal n.
C5 spinal n.
C7 vertebra
C8 spinal n.
T1 spinal n.
Intercostal n.
T12 spinal n.
L1 vertebra
L1 spinal n.
End of spinal cord
Cauda equina
L4 spinal n.
L5 vertebra
S1 spinal n.
Hip bone
Sacrum
Coccyx

CERVICAL PLEXUS (C1-C4) A
BRACHIAL PLEXUS (C5-T1) B
THORACIC NERVES (T1-T12) C
LUMBAR PLEXUS (L1-L4) D
SACRAL PLEXUS (L4, L5-S4) E

NERVE COVERINGS
EPINEURIUM F
PERINEURIUM G
ENDONEURIUM H
AXON I

POSTERIOR ROOT J
ANTERIOR ROOT K
THORACIC SPINAL NERVE C
POSTERIOR RAMUS L
LATERAL (MUSCULAR) BRANCH M
MEDIAL (CUTANEOUS) BRANCH N
ANTERIOR RAMUS O
(INTERCOSTAL NERVE) O
LAT. CUTANEOUS BR. F¹
ANT. CUTANEOUS BR. P

NERVE SECTION

PATTERN OF A TYPICAL THORACIC SPINAL NERVE
(Cross section through mid-thorax, viscera removed)

Cutaneous branch
Erector spinae muscles
Intervertebral foramen
Rami communicantes
Sympathetic ganglion
Spinal cord
Body of thoracic vertebra
Muscular branch
Skin
Innermost intercostal m.
Internal intercostal m.
External intercostal m.
Muscular branch
Transversus thoracic m.
Sternum
Superficial fascia
Cutaneous branch

CERVICAL PLEXUS & NERVES TO THE NECK

CN: Use dissimilar colors for A–E. Label C has been omitted to avoid confusion with C1–C5 (spinal nerves). (1) It will be helpful to follow the text as you color the large schematic. Color each C and its respective numeral, as well as the directional arrows. Where two roots form a nerve, that nerve (and its title) receives both colors. The phrenic nerve (F), formed by three nerves, receives its own color. (2) The sternocleidomastoid muscle, which lies above the spinal nerves, has been removed from the schematic but does appear in the cutaneous nerves illustration. A darkly outlined rectangle provides a frame of reference for the material covered in the schematic. (3) Color the four nerves of the cervical plexus, and C5 (bottom illustration).

CERVICAL PLEXUS

C1 SPINAL NERVE$_A$ & BRANCH$_{A'}$
ANSA CERVALICUS: SUP. ROOT$_{A^2}$

C2 SPINAL N.$_B$ & BR.$_{B'}$

C3 SPINAL N.$_D$ & BR.$_{D'}$
ANSA CERVALICUS: INF. ROOT$_{B^2+D^2}$
GREAT AURICULAR N. $_{B^3+D^3}$
LESSER OCCIPITAL N. $_{B^4+D^4}$
TRANSVERSE CERVICAL N. $_{B^5+D^5}$

C4 SPINAL N.$_E$ & BR.$_{E'}$
SUPRACLAVICULAR NS.$_{D^2+E^2}$

PHRENIC N.$_F$

ACCESSORY N. (XI CRANIAL)$_G$

C5 SPINAL N.$_H$ & BR.$_{H'}$
ROOT OF BRACHIAL PLEXUS$_{H^2}$

The distribution of spinal nerves from just below the neck to the lower abdomen is segmental and bilateral (Plate 86). In the neck and limbs, the distribution of spinal nerves is more irregular and occurs by way of interconnecting branches (*plexus*, a network) solely from the anterior rami.

The cervical plexus arises in the deep lateral neck, formed from the anterior rami of cervical nerves 1 through 4 (C1–C4). C1 sends a loop to C2; from this loop the deepest cervical muscles are innervated. Other C1 fibers pass along a length of the *hypoglossal (XII)* cranial nerve to supply the geniohyoid and thyrohyoid muscles. A branch of C1 (superior root of the *ansa cervicalis*) turns inferiorly from the hypoglossal nerve to descend to the level of C4, where it is joined by a confluence of fibers from the C2 and C3 spinal nerves (inferior root of the ansa). The fibers of this loop supply the infrahyoid muscles.

Fibers from C2 and C3 give origin to three important cutaneous nerves emerging from the anterior border of the mid-posterior triangle: the *great auricular* nerve destined for the external ear, the *lesser occipital* nerve to the posterolateral scalp, and the *transverse* (cutaneous) nerve of the neck supplying the skin and fascia over the anterior triangle (recall Plate 48).

Note that fibers from C3 and C4 send medial, intermediate, and lateral supraclavicular nerves to the skin in a broad area centered over the clavicle (anterolateral neck, shoulder, and anterior upper chest). They also project fibers to the trapezius muscle. Recall from Plate 83 that the primary nerve supply for this muscle is the spinal root of the *accessory (XI)* cranial nerve. Branches from C3 and C4 join with a branch from C5 to form the *phrenic* nerve, which innervates the thoracic diaphragm (recall Plate 50; see Plate 135). C5 is a major contributor to the upper trunk of the brachial plexus.

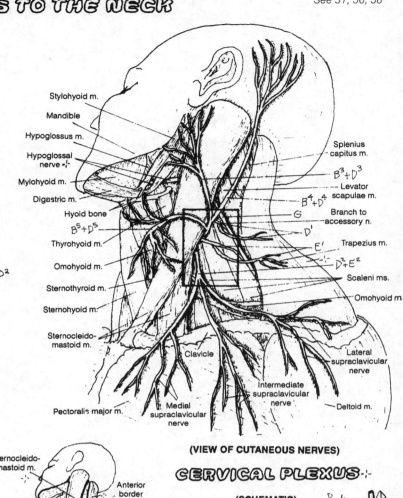

(VIEW OF CUTANEOUS NERVES)

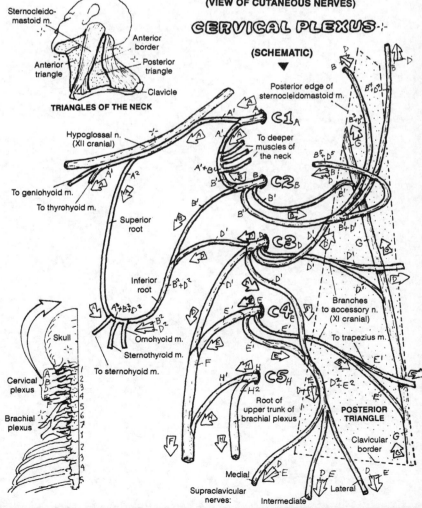

TRIANGLES OF THE NECK

CERVICAL PLEXUS

(SCHEMATIC)

BRACHIAL PLEXUS & NERVES TO THE UPPER LIMB

CN: Use light colors for A–D. (1) In the upper illustration, color the letters and numbers identifying the five roots of the brachial plexus. Note but do not color the small branches of the plexus as you color the plexus itself. Note in the lower illustration that the entire plexus is colored gray. (2) As you color each of the major nerves arising from the plexus, color it in the lower illustration as well. As you color each nerve, try to visualize it on your own limb.

BRACHIAL PLEXUS & MAJOR BRANCHES

ROOTS C5, C6 A
  UPPER TRUNK B
ROOT C7 A'
  MIDDLE TRUNK B'
ROOTS C8, T1 A²
  LOWER TRUNK B²

ANTERIOR DIVISION C
  LATERAL CORD (C5-C7) D
  MUSCULOCUTANEOUS N. E
  BR. TO MEDIAN N. F
  MEDIAL CORD (C8-T1) D'
  BR. TO MEDIAN N. F
  MEDIAN N. F'
  ULNAR N. G

POSTERIOR DIVISION (C5-T1) C'
  POSTERIOR CORD D²
  AXILLARY N. (C5-C6) H
  RADIAL N. (C5-T1) I

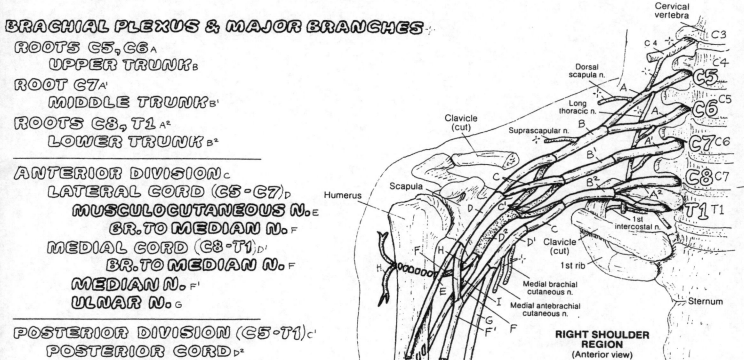

RIGHT SHOULDER REGION
(Anterior view)

The major nerves to the structures of the upper limb arise from the brachial plexus, formed from the anterior rami of spinal nerves C5–T1 (plus or minus one level). These rami form the *roots of the plexus.* In the pattern illustrated, further branching and joining of fibers in the neck, supraclavicular area, and axilla result in the formation of the five major nerves of the upper limb.

The brachial plexus is subject to injury (plexopathy) from excessive stretching or traction (e.g., rapid, forceful pulling of the upper limb) and compression (e.g., long-term placement of body weight on axillary or armpit cushions of crutches). In such injuries, there is great variation in degree of deficit, signs, and symptoms.

The musculocutaneous nerve (C5–C7) supplies the anterior arm muscles and is cutaneous in the forearm. Packaged in muscle, it is rarely traumatized. C5 and/or C6 nerve root compression can weaken these muscles. The *median nerve* (C5–C8, T1; "carpenter's nerve") supplies the anterior forearm muscles and the thenar muscles. It can be compressed at the carpal tunnel (recall Pl. 35), resulting in some degree of sensory deficit to fingers 1–3 and weakness in thumb movement (carpal tunnel

syndrome). Similar complaints can be associated with a C6 nerve root compression.

The ulnar nerve (C8–T1; "musician's nerve") supplies certain muscles of the forearm and most intrinsic muscles of the hand. It is subject to trauma as it rounds the elbow in the cubital tunnel, possibly resulting in ulnar-side finger pain, hand weakness, or abnormal little finger position. Similar complaints can be associated with a C8 nerve root compression. The *axillary nerve* (C5–C6) wraps around the neck of the humerus to supply deltoid and teres minor. It is vulnerable in fractures of the humeral neck, possibly resulting in a weak or paralyzed deltoid muscle. The *radial nerve* (C5–C8, T1) supplies the triceps, brachioradialis, and posterior forearm (extensor) muscles moving the wrist and hand. It is subject to damage as it rounds the mid-shaft of the humerus; significant nerve loss here results in "wrist drop" and loss of ability to work the hand (try moving your fingers with your wrist flexed hard). A C7 radiculopathy is characterized by a weak triceps, loss of the triceps jerk (reflex), and numbness of the middle finger. See the appendix for a listing of upper limb muscles and their nerve supply.

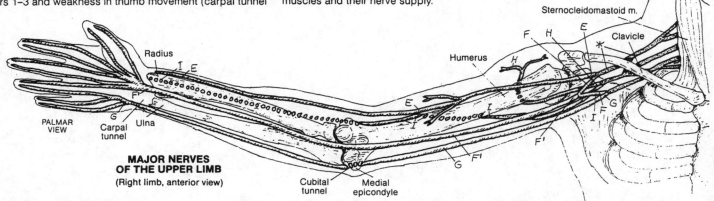

MAJOR NERVES OF THE UPPER LIMB
(Right limb, anterior view)

LUMBAR PLEXUS & NERVES TO THE LOWER LIMB

See 54, 56, 60

CN: Use a bright color for J. (1) Begin with the anterior view. Color the lumbar and sacral plexuses gray; note that they have been dotted for easy identification. Note the longest branch of the femoral nerve: saphenous nerve. (2) Color the posterior view, which includes almost entirely the sciatic nerve and its branches. The heel of the foot has been lifted to view the plantar nerves.

LUMBAR PLEXUS (L1-L4) *¹
FEMORAL N. A
SAPHENOUS N. B
OBTURATOR N. C
LAT. FEMORAL CUTAN. N. D

LUMBOSACRAL TRUNK (L4-L5) E

SACRAL PLEXUS (L4-S4) *²
POST. FEMORAL CUTAN. N. F
SUPERIOR GLUTEAL N. G
INFERIOR GLUTEAL N. H

SCIATIC N. (L4-S3) I
TIBIAL N. (L4-S3) J
MED. K LAT. PLANTAR N. K'
COMMON FIBULAR N. (L4-S2) L
SUPERFICIAL FIBULAR N. M
DEEP FIBULAR N. N

The lumbar plexus, formed from the anterior rami of L1–L4 spinal nerves, is located against the muscles of the posterior abdominal wall. The *femoral nerve* (L2–L4) passes through the psoas major muscle in its descent, emerging lateral to the muscle in the pelvis. As the nerve passes under the inguinal ligament, it lies on the muscle's anterior surface. The femoral nerve breaks up into a leash of nerves in the proximal thigh, supplying the four heads of the quadriceps femoris muscle and the sartorius muscle. Medially, the cutaneous *saphenous nerve* descends to the medial knee and beyond to the ankle. In mid-thigh, it passes through the adductor canal into the posterior femoral compartment, with the femoral artery and vein (recall Plate 63). The *obturator nerve* (L2–L4) passes along the lateral pelvic wall on the obturator internus muscle. It penetrates the obturator foramen to enter the medial thigh, supplying the adductor muscles. Both femoral and obturator nerves are subject to trauma or compression within the pelvis.

The *lumbosacral trunk* (L4, L5) joins with the sacral spinal nerves to form the *sacral plexus* (L4–S4). From this plexus, the *superior gluteal nerve* (L4, L5, S1) passes through the greater sciatic foramen, above the piriformis muscle, to supply gluteus medius (and sometimes minimus). The *inferior gluteal nerve* (L5, S1, S2) comes into the gluteal region above piriformis to supply gluteus maximus.

The *sciatic nerve* joins the posterior femoral cutaneous nerve and the inferior gluteal nerve to pass through the greater sciatic foramen under the piriformis muscle, deep to gluteus maximus (but not innervating it). It descends between the ischial tuberosity and the greater trochanter of the femur. Within the posterior femoral compartment, above the knee, the sciatic nerve splits into the tibial and common *fibular (peroneal) nerves*. The *tibial nerve* supplies the posterior leg muscles and the plantar muscles of the foot. The common fibular nerve supplies the lateral leg muscles (superficial fibular nerve) and the muscles of the anterolateral leg compartment (deep fibular nerve).

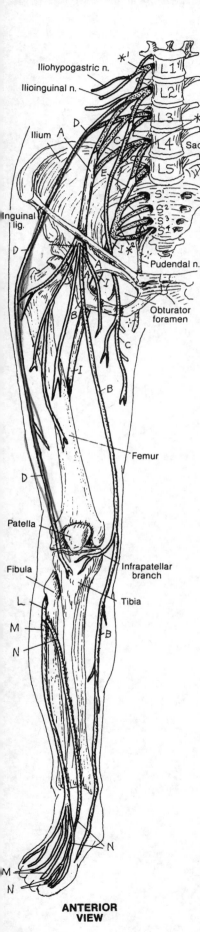

Iliohypogastric n.
Ilioinguinal n.
Ilium
Inguinal lig.
Pudendal n.
Obturator foramen
Femur
Patella
Fibula
Infrapatellar branch
Tibia

ANTERIOR VIEW

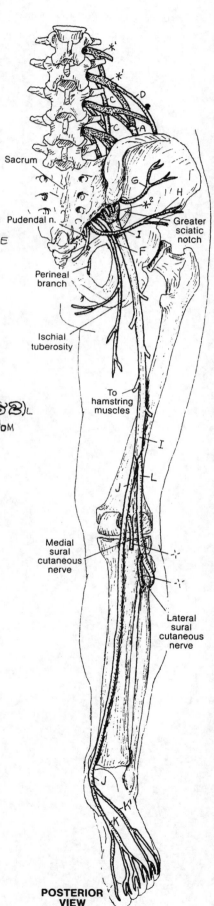

Sacrum
Pudendal n.
Perineal branch
Greater sciatic notch
Ischial tuberosity
To hamstring muscles
Medial sural cutaneous nerve
Lateral sural cutaneous nerve

POSTERIOR VIEW

DERMATOMES

CN: (1) Begin with the diagram at left, depicting sensory innervation of an area of skin (dermatome) and the degree of overlap among contiguous spinal nerve cutaneous branches and the dermatomes they supply. Color gray the three spinal nerves and the rectangular borders of the related dermatomes. Note the overlap. (2) Use very light colors for the five groups of dermatomes. Use one color for all dermatomes with the letter V, another color for the dermatomes marked with a C, and so on with T, L, and S. Suggestion: carefully outline the collection of C dermatomes with the color used for C, then color in the enclosed area, focusing on the skin areas serviced by the related spinal nerve; repeat with T, L, and S dermatomes.

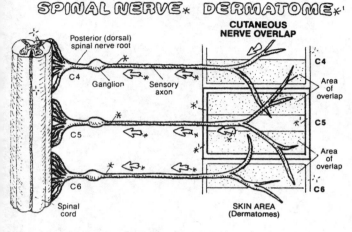

SPINAL NERVE* DERMATOME*'

DERMATOMES OF:

TRIGEMINAL NERVE v
V1 - V3 v

CERVICAL NERVES A
C2 - C8 A

THORACIC NERVES B
T1 - T12 B

LUMBAR NERVES c
L1 - L5 c

SACRAL NERVES D
S1 - S5 D

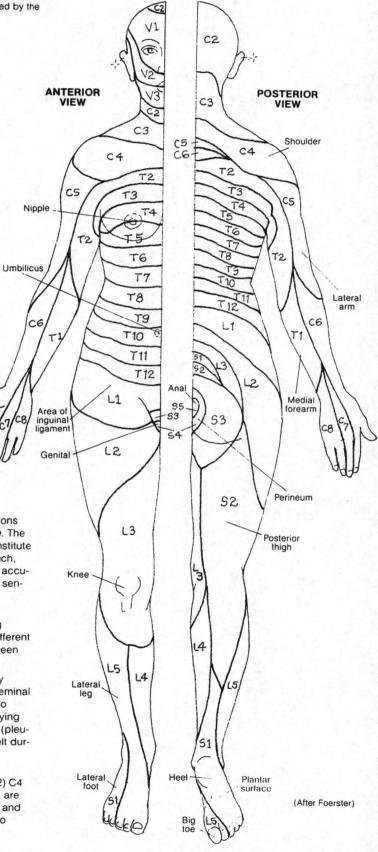

A dermatome is an area of skin (cutaneous area) supplied by the sensory axons of a single *spinal nerve* or a single division of the *trigeminal (V cranial) nerve*. The body surface is globally covered by sensory receptors. The dermatomes constitute a map of cutaneous innervation. Testing of general sensations (hot, cold, touch, pressure) and pain can help determine deficits in specific dermatomes. The accuracy of dermatomal representation has been corroborated in cases of spinal sensory root/nerve deficit (radiculopathy), trigeminal nerve irritation (trigeminal neuralgia), and spinal cord deficits (myelopathy).

In the case of spinal nerves and the trigeminal nerve, there is overlap among cutaneous branches of neighboring sensory axons. Thus, two branches of different spinal nerves or divisions of the trigeminal nerve cover the border zone between pairs of contiguous dermatomes.

In the case of pain, it is important to understand that dermatomes reflect only cutaneous pain and pain referred to the skin (e.g., visceral pain, spinal or trigeminal sensory nerve root pain). Commonly, pain of visceral origin may be referred to cutaneous areas served by the same spinal sensory nerve(s) as those supplying the visceral structure. For example, the pain of an inflamed lining of the lung (pleurisy), which is innervated by C3–C5 spinal nerves (phrenic nerve), may be felt during deep inspiration in the cervical dermatomes C3–C5 (usually along the supraclavicular nerve distribution).

Finally, note that (1) C1 has no dermatome because it has no sensory root; (2) C4 and T2 dermatomes overlap the chest wall because the spinal nerves C5–T1 are largely committed to the upper limb; and (3) the same is true in the low back and perineum with respect to spinal nerves L4–S2, which are largely committed to the lower limb.

SENSORY RECEPTORS

CN: Use your lightest colors for A and E. (1) Begin with the overview of a sensory pathway. (2) Color the general exteroceptors. Note that each receptor is connected to a sensory neuron (B) of a different color. (3) Color the proprioceptors in the lower illustration. Color over the entire muscle spindle, but not the surrounding muscle fibers.

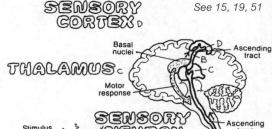

SENSORY CORTEX D

THALAMUS C

SENSORY NEURON B

RECEPTOR A

Basal nuclei

Motor response

Stimulus

Ascending tract

Ascending tract

Spinal cord

SENSORY PATHWAY
(Schematic)

Sensory receptors provide information to the brain about the internal and external environment of the body. Most receptors are transducers: they convert mechanical, chemical, electrical, or light stimuli to electrochemical impulses that can be conducted by the nervous system. Once generated, informational or sensory impulses travel to the CNS via sensory neurons, ultimately reaching the thalamus. Here impulses are relayed to the sensory cortex (conscious interpretation) or to motor centers for appropriate (reflexive) response.

EXTEROCEPTORS -:-
SPECIAL N.S. -:-
GENERAL (CUTANEOUS) -:-
FREE NERVE ENDINGS / AXON D
MERKEL (TACTILE) CELL / AXON D'
ENCAPSULATED ENDINGS E-
MEISSNER (TACTILE) CORPUSCLE / AXON E'
RUFFINI (DEFORMATION) ENDINGS / AXON E²

Exteroceptors are located near the body surface. Special exteroceptors (not shown) include photoreceptors of the retina (light stimuli; Plate 95), taste receptors (chemical stimuli; Plate 100), and auditory receptors (sound stimuli; Plate 98). General exteroceptors are cutaneous sensory endings. They are either encapsulated or free. Free nerve endings, either single or in networks, are found in the epidermis and virtually all of the connective tissues of the body. Free endings may serve as thermoreceptors (heat/cold), mechanoreceptors (light touch), or pain receptors (nociceptors). Free endings may be specialized, as with the Merkel cell endings (see Plate 18) and the spiral endings around hair follicles sensitive to hair movement.

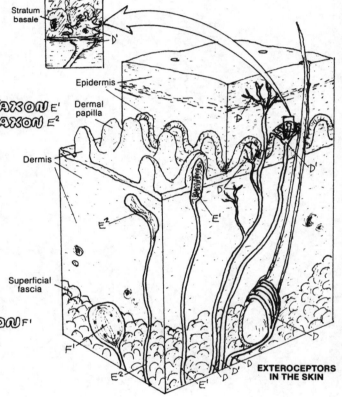

Stratum basale

Epidermis

Dermal papilla

Dermis

Superficial fascia

EXTEROCEPTORS IN THE SKIN

PROPRIOCEPTORS F-
PACINIAN (PRESSURE) CORPUSCLE / AXON F'
MUSCLE SPINDLE / MIXED AXONS F²
NEUROTENDINOUS ORGAN / AXON F³

Proprioceptors are found in deeper tissues (e.g., superficial fascia, deep fascia, tendons, ligaments, muscles, joint capsules) of the musculoskeletal system. They are sensitive to stretch, movement, pressure, and changes in position. The *Pacinian corpuscles* are large lamellar bodies acting as mechanoreceptors: distortion of their onion skin–like lamellae induces generation of an electrochemical impulse. *Muscle spindles*, sensitive to stretch, consist of two types of special muscle fibers (nuclear bag and nuclear chain) entwined with spiral or flower-spray sensory endings. Stretch of these spindles (and the skeletal muscle in which they are located) induces discharge in the sensory fibers. These impulses reach the cerebellum. Reflexive motor commands tighten the special muscle fibers and increase resistance of the skeletal muscle to stretch. By these spindles, the CNS controls muscle tone and muscle contraction. *Neurotendinous organs* (Golgi) are nerve endings enclosed in capsules located at muscle/tendon junctions or in tendons. They are induced to generate electrochemical impulses in response to tendon deformation or stretch.

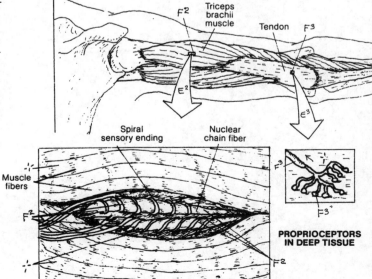

Triceps brachii muscle

Tendon

Spiral sensory ending

Nuclear chain fiber

Muscle fibers

PROPRIOCEPTORS IN DEEP TISSUE

INTEROCEPTORS N.S. -:-

Interoceptors (not shown) are free or encapsulated nerve endings, often in association with special epithelial cells, located in the walls of vessels and viscera. These receptors include chemoreceptors, baroreceptors (pressure), and nociceptors, They are not usually sensitive to the stimuli to which exteroceptors react.

SYMPATHETIC DIVISION (1)

CN: This plate is part one of a two-part presentation of the sympathetic division, and many structures with the same titles and subscripts on this and the next plate should receive the same color. (1) Begin with the schematic of the spinal cord segments containing the cell bodies of preganglionic neurons. These neurons (not shown) leave the spinal cord to enter or pass through the sympathetic chain. (2) Color the sympathetic chain and relations at upper right. (3) Color the pathways of the preganglionic and postganglionic neurons below. (4) Color the inset illustration.

SPINAL CORD SEGMENTS T1-L2 A
PREGANGLIONIC CELL BODY B
PREGANGLIONIC AXON B'
WHITE COMM. RAMUS C
SPLANCHNIC NERVE D
PREVERTEBRAL GANGLION E
SYMPATHETIC CHAIN F
POSTGANGLIONIC CELL BODY G
POSTGANGLIONIC AXON G'
GRAY COMM. RAMUS H*
SPINAL NERVE I

The autonomic nervous system (ANS; also visceral nervous system or VNS) is a part of the peripheral nervous system (PNS), responsible for the innervation of smooth muscle and glands in viscera and skin and of specialized cardiac muscle. It is a motor system uniquely characterized by two-neuron linkages and motor ganglia (pre- and post-ganglionic neurons). Sensory impulses from viscera are conducted by typical sensory neurons not generally described with the ANS but considered part of the VNS. The sympathetic (thoracolumbar) division of the ANS is concerned with degrees of "fight or flight" responses to stimuli: pupillary dilatation, increased heart and respiratory rates, increased blood flow to brain and skeletal muscles, and other related reactions.

The cell bodies of preganglionic neurons are restricted to the lateral horns of the *spinal cord segments T1 through L2*. The axons of these neurons leave the cord via the anterior roots, join with *spinal nerves* for a very short distance, and turn medially to enter the *sympathetic chain of ganglia* via the *white communicating rami* (white because the axons are myelinated and "white"). The chain is located bilaterally alongside the vertebral column (see inset illustration). Once in the chain, the preganglionic axons can take one or more of four courses: (1) synapse with the *postganglionic neuron* at the same level it entered the chain; (2) ascend and synapse at a higher level of the chain; (3) descend and synapse at a lower level of the chain; (4) pass straight through the chain, forming a nerve that runs from the chain to the front of the vertebral column (splanchnic nerve), and synapse with a *postganglionic neuron* there (*prevertebral ganglia*).

The postganglionic neuron within the chain leaves via the *gray communicating ramus* to join the *spinal nerve*. There are gray rami bilaterally at every segment of the spinal cord; white rami exist only from T1 to L2. Gray rami are so called because the resident axons are unmyelinated and collectively have a duller color than those of the white rami. Postganglionic axons from prevertebral ganglia travel in a plexus configuration to the viscus they supply. Plate 92 puts this division into a more meaningful perspective.

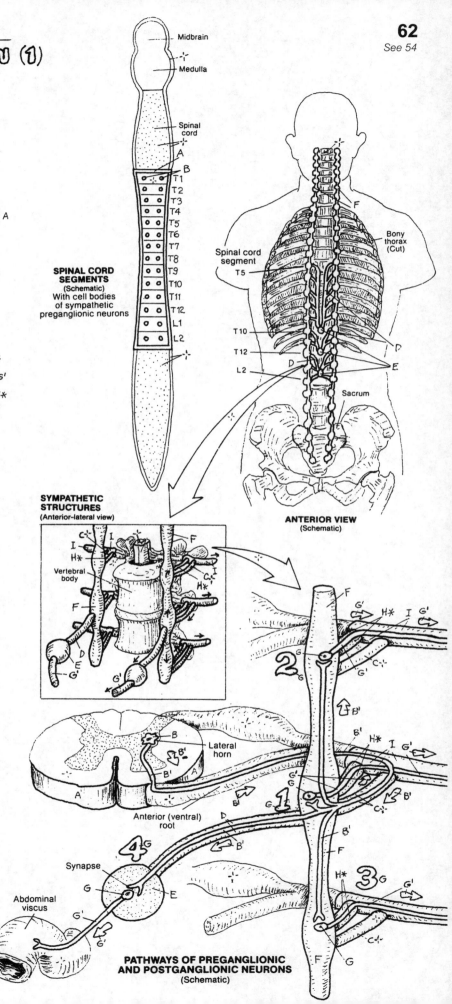

SPINAL CORD SEGMENTS (Schematic) With cell bodies of sympathetic preganglionic neurons

ANTERIOR VIEW (Schematic)

SYMPATHETIC STRUCTURES (Anterior-lateral view)

Vertebral body

PATHWAYS OF PREGANGLIONIC AND POSTGANGLIONIC NEURONS (Schematic)

Lateral horn

Anterior (ventral) root

Synapse

Abdominal viscus

SYMPATHETIC DIVISION (2)

See 62

CN: Use the same colors as you used on the preceding plate for preganglionic neurons (B), splanchnic nerves (D), and postganglionic neurons (G), all of which have been given the subscripts they had on Plate 92. First orient yourself to this diagram. Note the spinal cord in the center with sympathetic chains of ganglia on either side. Not all connections of both chains are shown. Here, the pathways on the left are to the skin. Pathways on the right are to viscera in the head and body cavities. Start with the preganglionic neurons on the left (B) and color the chain and related parts (G, G³) on the left. Then read the related text. Color the preganglionic neurons (B) on the right and the splanchnic nerves (D) to the abdominal viscera. Color the postganglionics (G, G¹, G²) to the head and thorax, and then the postganglionics (G⁴, G⁵) from the prevertebral ganglia to the abdominal and pelvic/perineal organs.

PREGANGLIONIC NEURONS_B
SPLANCHNIC N._D
POSTGANGLIONIC NEURONS_G
TO HEAD & NECK G¹
TO THORACIC VISCERA G²
TO SKIN G³
SWEAT GLANDS G³
ARRECTOR PILI G³
BLOOD VESSELS G³
TO ABDOMINAL VISCERA G⁴
TO PELVIC/
PERINEAL VISC._G⁵

Sympathetic innervation of skin (and viscera as well) begins with the *preganglionic neurons* in the thoracolumbar part of the spinal cord. The axons leave the cord via the anterior rami of spinal nerves, enter and leave the spinal nerves to join the white communicating rami. These rami bring the axons into the sympathetic chain. Axons from the upper thoracic cord ascend the chain up to the highest ganglion (superior cervical ganglion at the level of the first cervical vertebra). Axons from the lower thoracic and upper lumbar cord enter the chain and descend as far as the lowest ganglion (ganglion impar at the level of the coccyx). At every level of the chain (roughly coincident with spinal cord segments), the preganglionic axons synapse with *postganglionic neurons*. The postganglionic axons leave the chain via the gray communicating rami, enter the spinal nerves from C1 through Co1, and reach the skin via cutaneous branches of these nerves. These axons induce secretory activity in sweat glands, contraction of arrector pili muscles, and vasoconstriction in skin arterial vessels.

Postganglionics to the head (vessels and glands) leave the superior cervical ganglia and entwine around arteries enroute to the head (in the absence of spinal nerves) to reach their target organs. *Postganglionics to the heart and lungs* leave the upper ganglia of the chain, reaching these organs via cardiac nerves and the pulmonary plexus. These neurons act on heart muscle and the cardiac conduction system to increase heart rate; they induce relaxation of bronchial musculature, facilitating easier breathing.

Preganglionics to abdominal and pelvic viscera leave the cord at levels T5–L2, enter the white communicating rami, and pass through the sympathetic chain without synapsing. They form three pairs of *splanchnic nerves* between the chain and the prevertebral ganglia on the aorta. These axons synapse with the postganglionic neurons in the prevertebral ganglia. The axons of these neurons reach for smooth muscle, inducing contraction of sphincters and decreasing intestinal motility, relaxing bladder muscle and constricting the urinary sphincter. These axons stimulate the adrenal medulla to secrete mostly epinephrine and some norepinephrine, stimulate secretion of glands and muscle contraction in the male genital ducts (ejaculation), and stimulate uterine contractions.

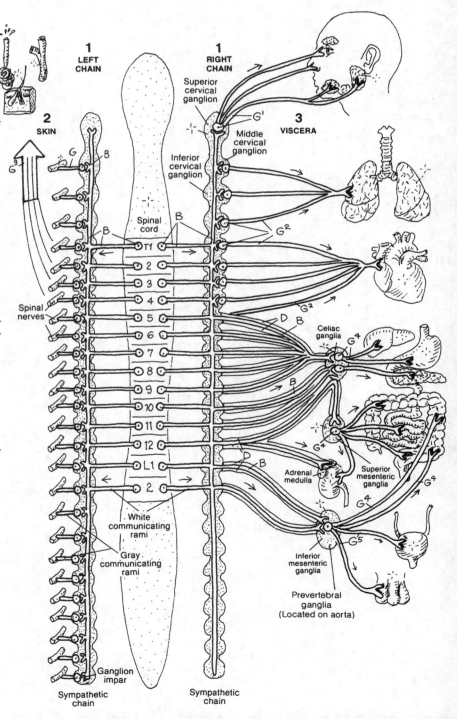

SYMPATHETIC DIVISION
(Schema showing the following)

1 Bilateral chains of ganglia with white rami connections to spinal cord.
  Each chain has both connections (**2**) and (**3**), and they are mirror-images of one another.
2 Left chain with postganglionic connections to skin.
3 Right chain with splanchnic nerves/postganglionic connections to viscera.

1 LEFT CHAIN

1 RIGHT CHAIN

Superior cervical ganglion

G¹

Middle cervical ganglion

Inferior cervical ganglion

2 SKIN

3 VISCERA

G³

G

B

Spinal cord

B

G²

Spinal nerves

B

T1
2
3
4
5
6
7
8
9
10
11
12
L1
2

D B

Celiac ganglia

G⁴

G²

D B

G⁴

Adrenal medulla

Superior mesenteric ganglia

G⁵

White communicating rami

Gray communicating rami

Inferior mesenteric ganglia

Prevertebral ganglia
(Located on aorta)

Ganglion impar

Sympathetic chain

Sympathetic chain

PARASYMPATHETIC DIVISION

CN: Continue using the same colors you used on Plates 91 and 92 for subscripts B, D, and G. Use a bright color for E. This drawing shows the parasympathetic scheme on one side of the body only (nerve distribution is identical for both sides). (1) Start with the preganglionic neurons in the head and work through the postganglionic neurons, noting the structures innervated. Note particularly the extensive pattern associated with the vagus nerve. (2) Continue with the sacral preganglionics and postganglionics, noting the target organs. (3) Color the diagram describing ganglia location in the two ANS divisions.

PREGANGLIONIC NEURONS.
III CRANIAL N. B¹
VII CRANIAL N. B²
IX CRANIAL N. B³
X CRANIAL B⁴
PELVIC SPLANCHNIC N. D
GANGLIA E
CILIARY E¹
PTERYGOPALATINE E²
SUBMANDIBULAR E³
OTIC E⁴
INTRAMURAL E⁵
POSTGANGLIONIC NEURONS.
EYE G¹
NASAL/ORAL CAVITIES G²
SALIVARY GLANDS G³
THORACIC/ABDOMINAL VISC. G⁴
PELVIC/PERINEAL VISCERA G⁵

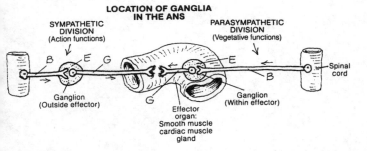

LOCATION OF GANGLIA IN THE ANS

SYMPATHETIC DIVISION (Action functions)

PARASYMPATHETIC DIVISION (Vegetative functions)

Ganglion (Outside effector)

Effector organ: Smooth muscle cardiac muscle gland

Ganglion (Within effector)

Spinal cord

The parasympathetic division of the ANS is concerned with vegetative functions—e.g., it encourages secretory activity on the body's mucous and serous membranes, promotes digestion by increased peristalsis and glandular secretion, and induces contraction of the urinary bladder.

The parasympathetic preganglionic neuronal cell bodies in the head are located in the brain stem associated with certain cranial nerves. The preganglionic axons leave the brain stem with their cranial nerve and synapse at one of the cranial *ganglia*. The *postganglionic neurons* tend to be short, terminating in salivary glands and other glands of the nasal and oral cavities. The preganglionic fibers associated with the *vagus (X cranial) nerve* are unusually long, descending the neck, the esophagus, and through the esophageal hiatus to the gastrointestinal tract. The axons of these neurons extend as far as the descending colon. The ganglia are in the muscular walls of the organ they supply (*intramural ganglia*); the postganglionic axons are very short, terminating in smooth muscle and glands.

The cell bodies of the sacral preganglionic neurons are located in the lateral horns of sacral segments 2, 3, and 4 of the spinal cord. Their axons leave the cord via the anterior rami but form their own nerves, called the *pelvic splanchnic nerves* (nervi erigentes). These nerves project to the pelvis, mix with sympathetic postganglionics in the pelvic plexus, and depart for their target organs. They synapse with the postganglionic neurons in intramural ganglia in the walls of the organ supplied. These fibers stimulate contraction of rectal and bladder musculature and induce vasodilatation of vessels to the penis and clitoris (erection).

The parasympathetic and sympathetic divisions of the autonomic nervous system are not antagonistic. Their respective activities are coordinated and synchronized to achieve dynamic stability of body function during a broad range of life functions, such as eating, running, fear, or relaxation.

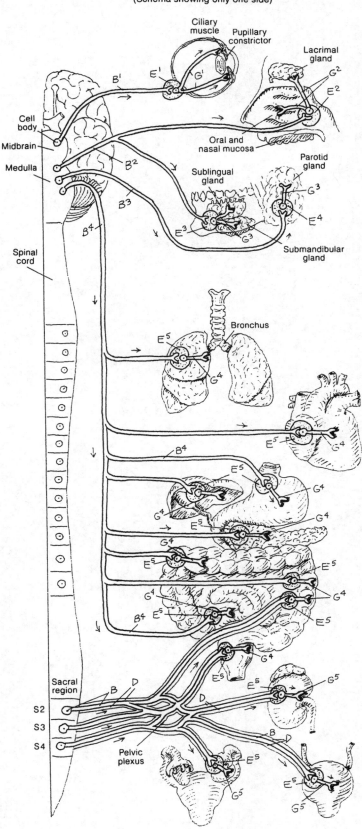

PARASYMPATHETIC DIVISION
(Schema showing only one side)

BLOOD VESSELS

CN: Use red for A, purple for B, blue for C, and very light colors for D, F, and H. (1) Complete the upper left diagram, beginning with the large arteries. (2) Color the blood vessels and their titles at the bottom of the plate. Note that the vas and nervus vasorum in the fibrous tissue layer (H) are not colored. (3) In the diagram of venous valve action, the blood in both vein and artery is colored gray.

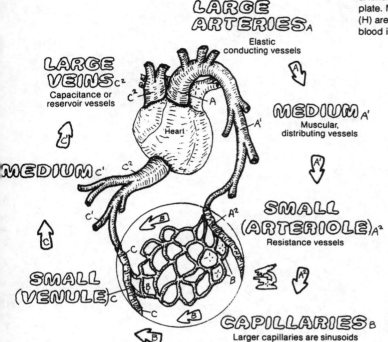

LARGE ARTERIES A
Elastic conducting vessels

LARGE VEINS C²
Capacitance or reservoir vessels

MEDIUM A'
Muscular, distributing vessels

MEDIUM C'

Heart

SMALL (ARTERIOLE) A²
Resistance vessels

SMALL (VENULE) C

CAPILLARIES B
Larger capillaries are sinusoids

Large arteries (elastic or conducting arteries), such as the aorta or common carotid, contain multiple layers of elastic tissue. They are roughly the size of a finger. *Medium arteries* (muscular, distributing arteries), averaging the size of a pencil, are generally named (e.g., brachial). Diminutive branches of medium arteries are called small arteries (*arterioles*); unnamed, they control the flow of blood into capillary beds (resistance vessels). *Capillaries* are unnamed simple endothelial tubes supported by thin fibrous tissue. Microscopic in dimension, some capillaries are larger (sinusoids) or more specialized than others.

Veins get progressively larger as they get closer to the heart. Veins have tributaries; except in portal circulations, they do not have branches. Venules (small veins) are formed by the merging of capillaries and are basically of the same construction. *Venules* merge to form *medium veins*, and these are the tributaries of *large veins* (capacitance or reservoir vessels). Certain specialized large veins, as in the skull, are called sinuses. The walls of these veins are thinner than those of their arterial counterparts, and their lumens are generally larger. Large veins can stretch significantly, becoming virtual reservoirs of blood.

All vessels demonstrate a simple squamous epithelial (endothelial) lining (tunica interna) supported by a thin layer of fibrous tissue (not shown). Most medium veins of the neck and extremities have a series of small pockets formed from the endothelial layer. These valves are paired and point in the direction of blood flow. Though offering no resistance to blood flow, they will bend into and close off the lumen of the vein when the flow of blood is reversed. Valves resist gravity-induced blood pooling, especially in the lower limb vessels. Venous flow here is enhanced by the contraction of skeletal muscles, whose bulges give an anti-gravity boost to the movement of blood. The *internal elastic lamina*, a discrete layer only in medium-sized arteries, assists in maintaining blood pressure; this tissue is more diffuse in other vessels. The *tunica media* consists of concentrically arranged smooth muscle fibers. It is well developed in medium arteries, least developed in veins. Medium arteries use this layer in distributing blood from one field to another. In arterioles, reduced to only one or two layers, the smooth muscle can literally block blood flow into capillary fields. The *external elastic lamina* exists as a discrete layer only in muscular arteries. The *tunica externa* (adventitia) is fibrous tissue contiguous with the fascial layer in which the vessel is located; within this tunica, much smaller nutrient vessels (vasa vasorum) and motor nerves (nervi vasorum) are found. In very specialized situations, the structure of small vessels may be specially adapted—e.g., the glomerulus, in Plate 149.

VESSEL STRUCTURE *
TUNICA INTERNA :
ENDOTHELIUM D
INTERNAL ELASTIC LAMINA E
TUNICA MEDIA :
SMOOTH MUSCLE F
EXTERNAL ELASTIC LAMINA G
TUNICA EXTERNA :
FIBROUS TISSUE H

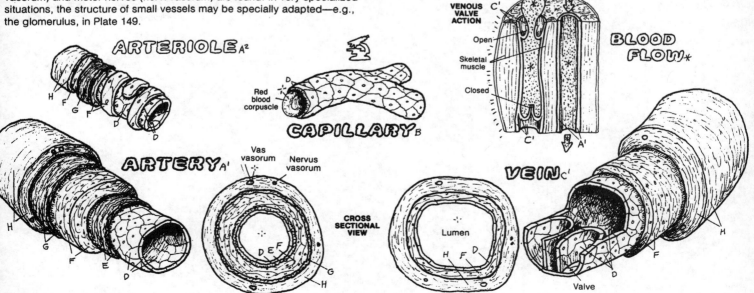

ARTERIOLE A²

CAPILLARY B

Red blood corpuscle

VENOUS VALVE ACTION

Open

Skeletal muscle

Closed

BLOOD FLOW *

ARTERY A'

Vas vasorum

Nervus vasorum

CROSS SECTIONAL VIEW

VEIN C'

Lumen

Valve

CHAMBERS OF THE HEART

CN: Use blue for A–A⁴, red for H–H⁴, and your lightest colors for B, C, I, and J. All dotted arrows (A⁴) receive a blue color; all clear arrows (H⁴) receive a red color. (1) Begin with the arrows A⁴ above the title list and above the superior vena cava (A) in the illustration at upper right and color the structures in the order of the title list (A–H³). (2) Color the circulation chart at lower right, beginning with the arrow A⁴ leading into the right atrium (numeral 1). Color the numerals in order from 1 to 4 and related arrows. Do not color the chambers or the vessels in this drawing at lower right.

SUPERIOR VENA CAVA ₐ
INFERIOR VENA CAVA ₐ'
RIGHT ATRIUM ₈

RIGHT VENTRICLE c
  A-V TRICUSPID VALVE ᴅ
    CHORDAE TENDINEAE ₑ
    PAPILLARY MUSCLE ꜰ

PULMONARY TRUNK ₐ²
  PUL. SEMILUNAR VALVE ɢ
  PUL. ARTERY ₐ³
PULMONARY VEIN ₕ
LEFT ATRIUM ᵢ

LEFT VENTRICLE ⱼ
  A-V BICUSPID (MITRAL) VALVE ᴅ'
    CHORDAE TENDINEAE ₑ'
    PAPILLARY MUSCLE ꜰ'

ASCENDING AORTA ₕ'
  AORTIC SEMILUNAR VALVE ɢ'
  AORTIC ARCH ₕ²
  THORACIC AORTA ₕ³

The heart is the muscular pump of the blood vascular system. It contains four cavities (chambers): two on the right side (pulmonary heart), two on the left (systemic heart). The pulmonary "heart" includes the right atrium and right ventricle. The thin-walled *right atrium* receives poorly *oxygenated blood* from the *superior* and the *inferior vena cava* and from the *coronary sinus* (draining the heart vessels). The thin-walled *left atrium* receives richly *oxygenated blood* from pulmonary veins. Atrial blood is pumped at a pressure of about 5 mm Hg into the *right and left ventricles* simultaneously through the atrioventricular orifices, guarded by the 3-cusp *tricuspid valve* on the right and the 2-cusp *bicuspid valve* on the left. The cusps are like panels of a parachute, secured to the *papillary muscles* in the ventricles by tendinous *chordae tendineae*. These muscles contract with the ventricular muscles, tensing the cords and resisting cusp over-flap as ventricular blood bulges into them during ventricular contraction (systole). The right ventricle pumps oxygen-deficient blood to the lungs via the *pulmonary trunk* at a pressure of about 25 mm Hg (right ventricle), and the left ventricle pumps oxygen-rich blood into the *ascending aorta* at a pressure of about 120 mm Hg simultaneously. This pressure difference is reflected in the thicker walls of the left ventricle compared to the right. The pocket-like *pulmonary and aortic semilunar valves* guard the trunk and aorta, respectively. As blood falls back toward the ventricle from the trunk/aorta during the resting phase (diastole), these pockets fill, closing off their respective orifices and preventing reflux into the ventricles.

**ANTERIOR VIEW
OF HEART CAVITIES
AND GREAT VESSELS**

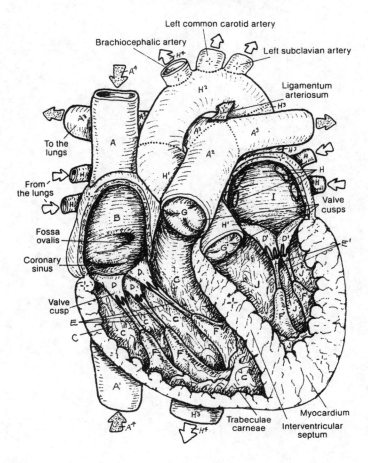

**CIRCULATION
THROUGH
THE HEART**

OXYGEN-RICH BLOOD H⁴ ▷
OXYGEN-POOR BLOOD A⁴ ▷

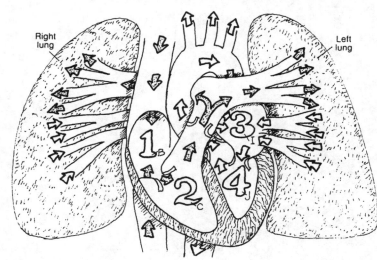

ARTERIES OF THE HEAD & NECK

CN: Use red for A and dark or bright colors for B and L. (1) Begin with the brachiocephalic (A) and the right subclavian (B) and its branches. Color the broken lines that represent deeper vessels. (2) Color the anterior view revealing the absence of the brachiocephalic artery on the left side. (3) Color the arrows pointing to the four sites where the arterial pulse may be palpated.

BRACHIOCEPHALIC_A

RIGHT SUBCLAVIAN_B
　INTERNAL THORACIC_C
　VERTEBRAL_D
　THYROCERVICAL TRUNK_E
　　INFERIOR THYROID_F
　　SUPRASCAPULAR_G
　　TRANSVERSE CERVICAL_H
　COSTOCERVICAL TRUNK_I
　　DEEP CERVICAL_J
　　HIGHEST INTERCOSTAL_K

RIGHT COMMON CAROTID_L
　INTERNAL CAROTID_M
　　OPHTHALMIC_N
　EXTERNAL CAROTID_O
　　SUPERIOR THYROID_P
　　LINGUAL_Q
　　FACIAL_R
　　OCCIPITAL_S
　　MAXILLARY_T
　　　ALVEOLAR BRANCHES: INF._U SUP._U'
　　　MIDDLE MENINGEAL_V
　　　POSTERIOR AURICULAR_W
　　SUPERFICIAL TEMPORAL_X
　　　TRANSVERSE FACIAL_Y

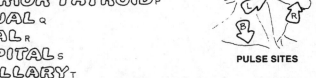

PULSE SITES

The subclavian artery is the major source of blood to the upper limb, and it contributes vessels to the lateral and posterior neck and shoulder. On the right, the artery springs from the brachiocephalic; on the left, the artery comes directly off the aortic arch, as does the common carotid (see below). The *vertebral artery* dives deep into the neck to enter the transverse foramen of the 6th cervical vertebra. It supplies vessels to the spinal cord, brain stem, and cerebellum. The *thyrocervical trunk* arises just medial to the anterior scalene muscle (see Plate 48) and immediately gives off its branches, the destinations of which are obvious by name. The subclavian artery ends and the axillary artery begins at the lateral border of the first rib.

The common carotid artery ascends the neck ensheathed with the internal jugular vein and vagus nerve (not shown). Between the hyoid bone and the upper thyroid cartilage, the artery bifurcates into *internal* and *external carotid arteries*. The internal carotid passes into the skull, gives off the *ophthalmic artery* to the orbital region, and joins the circulus arteriosus (Plate 109). The external carotid artery and its branches supply all of the visceral, musculoskeletal, and dental structures of the head and neck less the brain and orbit. The external carotid divides into *maxillary* and *superficial temporal arteries*. The maxillary artery is a major source of blood to the deep skull cavities, the orbit, teeth, the muscles of mastication, and the dura mater (*middle meningeal artery*). The middle meningeal artery on the dura mater immediately deep to the temporal bone is a potential site of rupture with a hard fall on the side of the head (epidural hematoma).

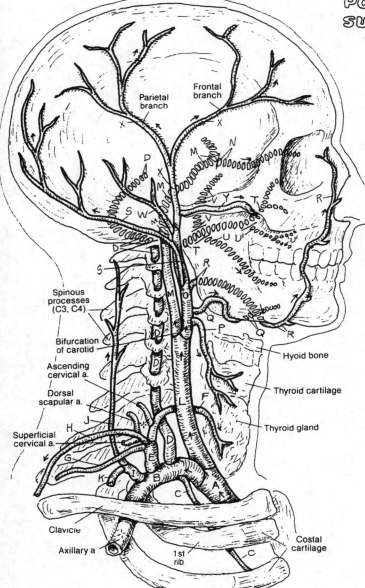

Frontal branch
Parietal branch

Spinous processes (C3, C4)
Bifurcation of carotid
Ascending cervical a.
Dorsal scapular a.
Superficial cervical a.

Hyoid bone
Thyroid cartilage
Thyroid gland

Clavicle
Axillary a
1st rib
Costal cartilage

LEFT SUBCLAVIAN ARTERY_B'
LEFT COMMON CAROTID A._L'

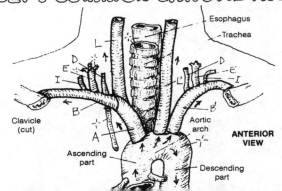

Esophagus
Trachea

Clavicle (cut)
Aortic arch
ANTERIOR VIEW
Ascending part
Descending part

LYMPHOCYTE CIRCULATION

CN: Use blue for H, red for I, purple for L, and green for M. (1) Color over the light lines representing peripheral (superficial) lymph vessels (A). (2) Color each large step numeral in the diagram below with the related titles. In the bottom diagram, do not color the lymphocytes circulating in and between the blood and lymph capillaries.

SUPERFICIAL DRAINAGE:-
PERIPHERAL LYMPH VESSELS A
CERVICAL NODE B
AXILLARY NODE B'
INGUINAL NODE B²

DEEP DRAINAGE:-
LYMPHATIC TRUNK C
CYSTERNA CHYLI D
THORACIC DUCT E
RIGHT LYMPH DUCT F

The body is about 60% fluid (by volume), which fills cells, vessels, and spaces. Fluid requires circulation. Some of the fluid of the blood and some lymphocytes leave the circulatory system and enter the tissue spaces. Some of this fluid (lipids) and lymphocytes (lymph) are recovered by thin-walled vessels (*lymphatic capillaries*) that form in the loose connective tissue spaces. Unlike the closed-loop blood capillary networks, these tiny vessels are closed at one end. They merge to form progressively larger lymphatic vessels that drain into large veins in the neck. These vessels constitute the lymphatic system. Certain lymphatic vessels enter and leave lymph-filtering stations called *lymph nodes*.

Region-draining *lymph trunks* converge into a dilated lymph sac (*cysterna chyli*) lying deep to the abdominal aorta on the first lumbar vertebra. The *thoracic duct* begins at the upper end of the sac, ascends the anterior surface of the vertebral column, and drains into the left subclavian vein at its junction with the internal jugular vein. The *right lymph duct* terminates similarly on the opposite side. It drains the dotted area.

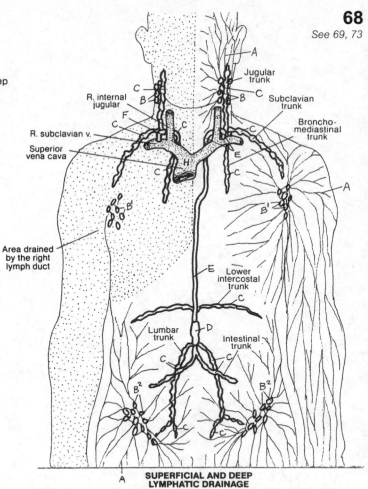

SUPERFICIAL AND DEEP LYMPHATIC DRAINAGE

LYMPHOCYTE CIRCULATION:-
GENERATIVE ORGAN G
VENOUS BLOOD H
ARTERIAL BLOOD I
LYMPHOID TISSUE J
PERIPHERAL TISSUE K
CAPILLARY NETWORK L
LYMPH VESSEL M
LYMPH NODE M'

Lymphocytes are among the principal cells of the immune system. The circulation scheme reveals the primary pathway for the dissemination of lymphocytes from their *generative organs* (*bone marrow, thymus*) into the *lymphoid tissues* and organs as well as organs and tissues in general (*peripheral tissues*). Such a circulation pattern provides for maximum exposure of lymphocytes to microorganisms and subsequent body defense operations (immune responses).

Formed and developed in the bone marrow and thymus (1), lymphocytes leave with the *venous blood* to enter the circulation. By way of *arterial blood* (2), lymphocytes enter the *capillary networks* of the lymphoid tissues (3) and other peripheral tissues (4). The lymphocytes may remain in or migrate from the lymphoid organs/peripheral tissues, entering blood capillaries or lymph vessels. From lymph capillaries, the lymphocytes flow with the lymph fluid into regional lymph nodes (5). Here they may become resident or they may depart the node and merge with other lymph vessels to join the lymph ducts (6) that connect with the blood circulatory system.

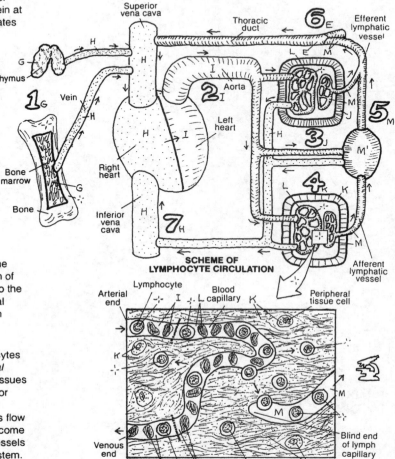

SCHEME OF LYMPHOCYTE CIRCULATION

IMMUNE (LYMPHOID SYSTEM)

INTRODUCTION

CN: Use green for D, the same colors for bone marrow (A) and thymus (B) used on Plate 121. (1) Structures depicting mucosal-associated lymphoid tissue (E) are generalizations; more accurate representations can be seen on Plate 127. (2) The three lymphocyte types have identifying letters drawn into their nuclei. Color over the entire cell in all cases. (3) The various types of cells appearing in this section will generally be identified by more descriptive letters/labels (e.g., PC = plasma cell). Try to use the same light color for each type wherever it appears on plates 122–128.

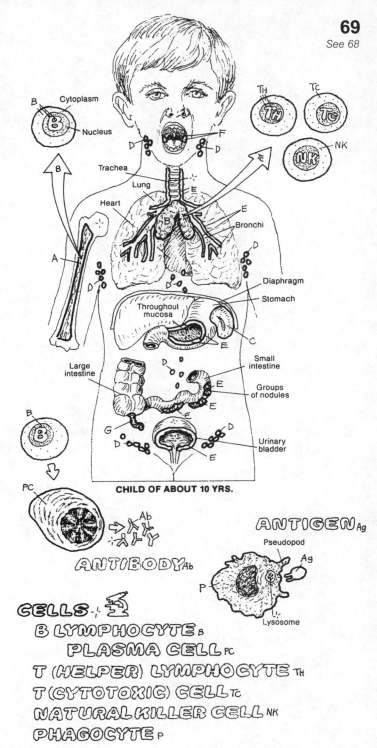

CHILD OF ABOUT 10 YRS.

PRIMARY ORGANS:
BONE MARROW A
THYMUS B

The lymphoid system, the anatomical component of the immune system, functions in defense against microorganisms entering the body as well as the destruction of cells or cell parts no longer recognizable as "self." Lymphoid tissues and organs are predominantly collections of lymphocytes and related cells (see below), often supported by a meshwork of reticular fibers and cells.

The red bone marrow and thymus are primary lymphoid organs. The *bone marrow* contains the precursors of all lymphocytes and disburses lymphocytes into the circulation. It consists largely of great varieties of blood cells in various stages of maturation, phagocytes, reticular cells and fibers, and fat cells. Some of the lymphocytes mature and undergo structural and biochemical revision (differentiation) in the bone marrow to become B lymphocytes. Large lymphocytes enter the circulation from the bone marrow and function as natural killer cells. Some partly differentiated lymphocytes migrate via the blood to the thymus. There they become T cells and differentiate further. Those cells then re-enter the circulation and migrate to secondary lymphoid organs.

The thymus is located in the superior and anterior (inferior) mediastinum. It receives uncommitted lymphocytes from the bone marrow. The thymus is actively engaged in T lymphocyte proliferation and differentiation during embryonic and fetal life as well as the first decade of extrauterine life. The thymus begins to undergo degeneration (involution) after puberty.

SECONDARY ORGANS:
SPLEEN C
LYMPH NODE D
MUCOSAL ASSOCIATED LYMPHOID TISSUE (M.A.L.T.) E
TONSILS/ADENOIDS F
APPENDIX G

Secondary lymphoid organs are structures predominantly populated by lymphocytes that migrated from the primary lymphoid organs. The structural arrangement of these organs ranges from encapsulated, complex structures, like the *spleen* and *lymph nodes*, to a diffuse disposition of lymphocytes throughout the loose connective and epithelial tissues of the digestive system, if not all open cavities. These secondary organs represent satellite sites for lymphocytic activation when challenged by antigens. The *spleen* processes incoming blood. Its lymphocytes and phagocytes react rapidly to the presence of microorganisms and aged red blood corpuscles. *Lymph nodes* screen lymph from incoming (afferent) lymphatic vessels, much in the same manner as the spleen processes blood. Partly encapsulated, nodular masses of lymphoid tissue (tonsils and adenoids) guard the pharynx, marking incoming microorganisms for destruction. Unencapsulated, variably sized, nodular masses (follicles) of lymphocytes occur throughout the mucosal layers of open cavities (primarily the digestive tract), as do more diffuse distributions of lymphocytes. These unencapsulated follicles and lymphocyte collections constitute mucosal-associated lymphoid tissues (M.A.L.T.); in the intestines, they may be called "gut-associated lymphoid tissues" (G.A.L.T.). The vermiform appendix harbors multiple lymphoid follicles in its mucosa. The density of lymphocytes and follicles of lymphocytes in all these groups varies with the degree of immune responsivity required.

ANTIBODY Ab

ANTIGEN Ag

CELLS:
B LYMPHOCYTE B
PLASMA CELL PC
T (HELPER) LYMPHOCYTE TH
T (CYTOTOXIC) CELL TC
NATURAL KILLER CELL NK
PHAGOCYTE P

Activated B lymphocytes (B = bone marrow–derived) differentiate along specific lines, one of which becomes plasma cells. Plasma cells secrete protein molecules called antibodies into tissue fluids. Antibodies interact with and destroy antigens, a term restricted to those molecules (free or attached to/are part of cells and microorganisms) that elicit activation of the B cells.

Early T lymphocytes (T = thymus-derived) differentiate into one of a number of cells, including helper (TH), cytotoxic (TC), and memory cells (not shown). Activated by antigen stimulation, TH cells stimulate and regulate specific and nonspecific immune operations against cells, without necessarily being assisted by B cells. Thus, they are concerned with cell-mediated immunity. TC cells kill cells targeted by other T cells or lymphokines. Natural killer (NK) cells are neither B nor T cells. They are not activated by other cells or lymphokines (they kill naturally). In association with TC cells, they destroy tumor cells and virus-infected cells primarily. Phagocytes are cells that destroy antigen by phagocytosis. They function as antigen-presenting cells (APC) for T cells; T cells, in turn, activate phagocytes.

NATURAL & ACQUIRED IMMUNITY

CN: Use pink for IR and the same colors used on Plate 122 where possible. Radial lines surrounding a cell indicate activation. All elements shown have been magnified and schematized for coloring.

MICROORGANISM_A

NATURAL IMMUNITY

ANATOMIC BARRIER_ABa
COMPLEMENT_C
PHAGOCYTE_P
INFLAMMATORY RESPONSE_IR

Immunity is an anatomic and physiologic state of security against disease. *Natural* immunity exists independent of any specific microorganismal interaction with a lymphocyte. Shortly before birth and following, one progressively *acquires* a specific immunity following each lymphocyte's encounter with antigen and resulting activation. Phagocytes participate in both natural and acquired immunity; lymphocytes participate in acquired immunity and enhance natural immunity.

Natural immunity operates indiscriminately against *microorganisms* and degenerate cells/cell parts. *Anatomic barriers* (1), such as skin or mucous membranes, physically resist microorganismal invasion. *Phagocytes* approach their prey from the blood (2) or connective tissues (3), engulf them (4, phagocytosis), and destroy them with lysosomal enzymes (5). *Complement* (certain soluble proteins in body fluids) bind to microorganisms, enhancing their phagocytosis. Tissue irritation, e.g., disruption by a splinter, induces an inflammatory response that involves both natural and acquired immunity.

ACQUIRED IMMUNITY

Acquired immunity involves diverse but specific lymphocyte responses to the presence of *antigen*. A specific lymphocytic reaction to antigens (immune response) is characterized by the activation and proliferation of lymphocytes followed by the destruction of antigens. Two kinds of acquired immunity are possible, based on lymphocyte types: *humoral immunity* and *cellular immunity*. Inherent in both kinds of immunity are specificity and diversity of response, retention of cellular memory of antigen, and the ability to recognize self from non-self among the body's proteins.

ANTIGEN_Ag

HUMORAL IMMUNITY_B
B LYMPHOCYTE_B
MEMORY CELL_BM
PLASMA CELL_PC
ANTIBODY_Ab

INFECTED CELL_IC

CELLULAR IMMUNITY_T
T LYMPHOCYTE_T
MEMORY CELL_TM
HELPER CELL (TH)_TH
CYTOTOXIC CELL (TC)_TC

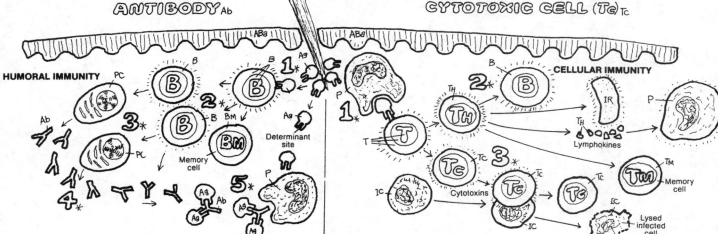

Humoral (fluid-related) immunity is characterized by *B lymphocytes* being activated by antigen (Ag) (1), proliferating, forming *memory cells* (BM), secreting antibody (Ab) (2), and forming *plasma cells (PC)* (3), which secrete *antibody* (4). Antibodies are complex proteins formed in response to a specific antigen and attached to it at the antigenic determinant site (5), facilitating its phagocytosis.

Cellular immunity is characterized by *T lymphocytes (T)* being activated by antigens attached to antigen-presenting cells: *phagocytes (P)* (1).

Most T cells differentiate into *helper T lymphocytes (TH)* and *cytotoxic T lymphocytes (TC)*. Helper T lymphocytes (2) enhance humoral immunity by activating B cells, augmenting the inflammatory response, activating phagocytes with stimulating factors (lymphokines), and forming *memory cells (TM)*. Cytotoxic T lymphocytes (3) bind to and destroy *infected cells* and form memory cells. Memory cells recognize specific structural characteristics of the antigens encountered ("memory") and facilitate rapid immune responses on subsequent exposure to those antigens.

THYMUS & RED MARROW

CN: Use red for G, blue for H, green for J. (1) Begin with red marrow (A) at the bottom of the plate. Then color the red marrow (K) portion of the newborn's arm bone. Color the thymus section and the diagrammatic description of lymphocyte maturation in the thymus. Note that the borders of the diagram represent the cortex and medulla of the thymus. Then color the schematic overview of thymic function.

THYMUS c
   FIBROUS SEPTA D
   CORTEX E
     UNDIFFERENTIATED LYMPHOCYTE U
     IMMATURE T LYMPHOCYTE I
  MEDULLA F
     MATURE T LYMPHOCYTE T
ARTERIAL VESSEL G
VENOUS VESSEL H
   SINUSOID H'
LYMPH VESSEL J

The thymus seeds the entire body with T lymphocytes, the protagonists of cellular immunity. It consists of two lobes of glandular tissue in the anterior and superior mediastinum. The thymus is functional and relatively large in the late fetus/newborn (15 gms), continues to grow and function during the pre-teen years, and declines in size and activity in the following years.

The functional thymus consists of microscopic lobules partitioned by *fibrous septa* containing blood vessels. Each lobule has an outer *cortex* dense with lymphocytes and a much less dense central *medulla*. The *epithelial cells* of the lobule form a structurally supporting "reticular" network. Distinctive concentric rings of keratinized epithelial cells (*Hassal's corpuscles*) are seen in the medulla; although associated with degenerative signs in aging, they may support lymphocyte differentiation. *Arterial vessels* bring *undifferentiated lymphocytes* into the cortex. The cells migrate into the medulla, showing signs of differentiating into T cells. In the inner cortex, the cells are largely *immature* (but committed) *T cells*. The medulla contains largely *mature T cells*. These cells leave the thymus by venules (*venous vessels*) to enter the systemic circulation. Some T lymphocytes enter *lymph vessels* destined for mediastinal lymph nodes and beyond. The thymus also produces a number of factors (hormones) stimulating lymphocyte differentiation.

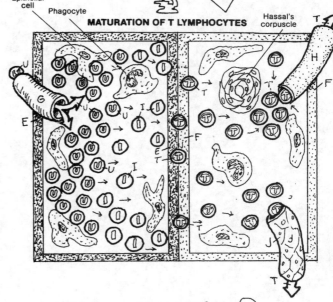

RED MARROW A
  LYMPHOCYTE STEM CELL L
  GROWTH FACTOR GF
  B LYMPHOCYTE B
  PRE-T CELL TP
  NATURAL KILLER CELL NK

Red marrow (recall Plate 20) is densely populated with a great variety of blood cells in various stages of development. The supporting framework of marrow is reticular fibers and cells. Fed by arterioles from the nutrient artery of the bone, the capillaries within the marrow are enlarged to the extent of being small sinuses (*sinusoids*). They reveal transient cytoplasmic "pores" for the immediate passage of cells into the circulation. Among the developing blood cells are *lymphocyte precursors*. These are stimulated to divide by certain *growth factors*. The progeny of these cells are mostly small and some large *lymphocytes*. B lymphocyte (B cell) maturation, natural killer cell (large lymphocyte) development, and pre–T cell development occur in the bone marrow. These lymphocytes enter the sinusoids and the venous outflow to be distributed bodywide.

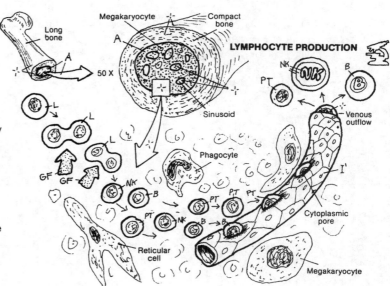

SPLEEN

CN: Use red for F and blue for H. Continue with the same colors as were used on preceding plates for the cells. (1) When coloring the schematic representation of spleen structures, note the underlying brackets that designate the structures fitting within the white pulp and red pulp regions. (2) Do not color the venous sinuses (G), in order to keep visible the gaps and highly branched reticular cells (lower illustration).

SPLEEN A
CAPSULE A'
TRABECULA C
WHITE PULP D
LYMPHOID FOLLICLE D'
RED PULP E

BLOOD VESSELS ·:·
ARTERY F
ARTERIOLE F'
VENOUS SINUSOID G·:·
VENULE H
VEIN H'

CELLS ·:·
T LYMPHOCYTE T
B LYMPHOCYTE B
MITOTIC LYMPHOCYTE ML
PHAGOCYTE P
PLASMA CELL PC

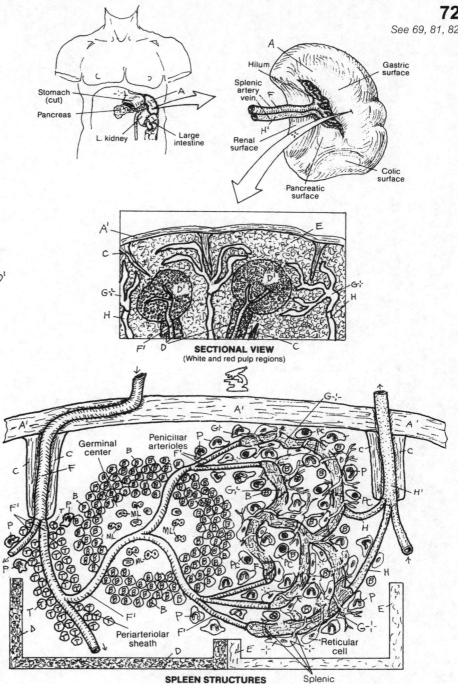

SECTIONAL VIEW
(White and red pulp regions)

SPLEEN STRUCTURES
(Schematic)

The soft, blood-filled, dark purple spleen lies posteriorly in the upper left abdominal quadrant, just above the left kidney, at about the level of the 11th and 12th ribs. It is generally about the size of your closed fist. The *capsule* of the spleen projects inward extensions (*trabeculae*) that support the organ and incoming/outgoing vessels. The microscopic view of the spleen is complicated by the endless sea of lymphocytes and phagocytes and, in this organ, red blood cells.

Small, downstream branches of the splenic artery travel in the fibrous trabeculae; branching *arterioles* become enveloped in lymphocytes (periarteriolar sheath) and branch among *lymphoid follicles*. These follicles, the arterioles, and their cellular sheaths constitute the *white pulp*. The follicles enlarge with antigenic stimulation; large *mitotic lymphocytes* (in various stages of cell division) begin to appear in the central part of each follicle (germinal center) following stimulation, creating a zone less dense than the surrounding, cell-packed area. As the straight (penicillar) arterioles leave the white pulp, they lose their muscular tunics to open into venous sinuses surrounded by phagocytes. These sinuses appear to have gaps amidst the

irregular strands of splenic cords (highly branched reticular cells, B cells, and plasma cells). Phagocytes hanging out among the branches engage aged red blood corpuscles that slip out of the sinuses. The sinuses and splenic cords constitute the red pulp. The sinusoids drain into venules, the tributaries of trabecular veins. These form the tributaries of the splenic veins.

Antibody production and phagocytosis are major activities of the spleen. As blood flows into the arterioles of the white pulp, antigen is greeted by phagocytes and myriad T cells, setting off cellular immune responses in the periarteriolar sheaths. Snaking into the follicles, the vessels are surrounded by B cells. Once activated by the presence of antigen, B cells transform into plasma cells, and antibody is produced (humoral immunity). Systemic infection markedly increases the output of lymphocytes, causing palpable splenic enlargement (splenomegaly). Removal of the spleen (splenectomy) is not a benign event. Absent splenic tissue, the body may have reduced immune capabilities.

LYMPH NODE

CN: Use red for M, blue for N, and green for O (if you have additional greens, use them on J–L); continue using the same colors for the various cells. (1) Color the circular insets identifying the dominant cell in the regions of the lymph node. In the paracortex, note the small circles representing venules (N¹).

LYMPH NODE A
CAPSULE A'
TRABECULA c
RETICULAR NETWORK D
CORTEX E
LYMPH FOLLICLE F
GERMINAL CENTER G
MEDULLA H
PARACORTEX I

LYMPH VESSELS ⫶
AFFERENT LYMPH VESSEL J
LYMPH SINUS K
EFFERENT LYMPH VESSEL L

BLOOD VESSELS ⫶
ARTERY M
VEIN N / VENULE N'

LYMPHOID CELLS ⫶
PHAGOCYTE P
T LYMPHOCYTE T
B LYMPHOCYTE B
MITOTIC LYMPHOCYTE ML
PLASMA CELL PC
LYMPH O
ANTIGEN Ag

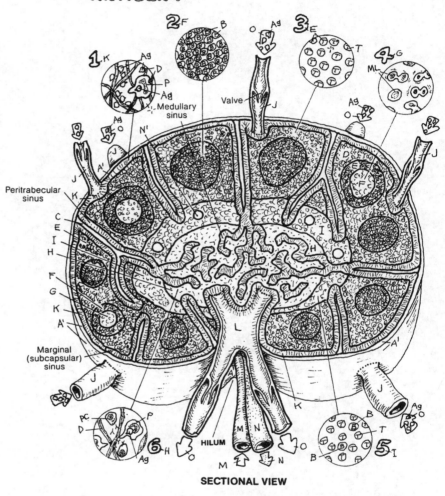

SECTIONAL VIEW

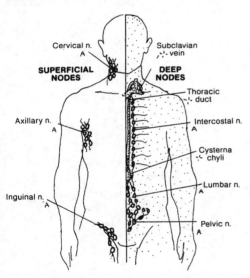

The lymph node has a fibrous *capsule* from which *trabeculae* invade the organ, dividing it incompletely into compartments. Fine reticular fibers and cells spread out from the trabeculae to form a thicket of interwoven branches throughout the node (*reticular network*). This intricate weave of fibers supports the dense populations of lymphocytes throughout the node. Lymph percolates through parts of the reticular network called *lymph sinuses* (only the marginal sinuses appear to be endothelial lined). The reticular fibers in these sinuses (1) form a spatial framework from which *phagocytes* can readily engage *antigens* in the lymph flow.

The node interior is characterized by an outer *cortex* and an inner *medulla*. The cortex reveals a group of particularly dense masses of B lymphocytes (2, *lymphoid follicles*) existing among a more sparse array of largely *T lymphocytes* in the interfollicular areas (3). In the presence of significant amounts of antigen, the follicles develop *germinal centers*; here are seen *mitotic lymphocytes* in varying degrees of mitosis (4). The outer part of the medulla (*paracortex*) has more diffuse arrangements of phagocytes, T cells, and some B cells (5). The endothelial cells of the venules in the paracortex are specialized and provide lymphocyte homing receptors that influence the localization of T and B cells within the node. The medulla contains a

concentrated array of interconnecting sinuses, with phagocytes and *plasma cells* in significant numbers (6).

Lymph enters the nodes by afferent vessels with valves controlling unidirectional traffic. As the lymph meanders through the throngs of reticular fibers in the sinuses, phagocytes pick off the antigens and present them to the T cells in the interfollicular areas. Activated B cells in the follicles, facilitated by helper (T$_H$) cells, transform into plasma cells and memory cells. The plasma cells and B cells secrete antibody with receptors that bind a portion of the antigen (antigenic determinant). Binding of antibody to the antigen facilitates destruction of the antigen. Major stimulus promotes the formation of germinal centers. Further immune activity occurs in the paracortical and inner medullary areas. Lymph leaves the medullary sinuses and the node by way of the *efferent vessels*. Lymphocytes also enter the node by small *arteries*; these cells can migrate into the sinuses from the venules while the remaining blood leaves the node by *veins*.

In summary, the lymph node is the site of both humoral-mediated (B cell) and cell-mediated (T cell) immune responses to antigens in the lymph. Palpable enlargement of cervical lymph nodes during an upper respiratory infection, for example, gives testimony to the existence of such mechanisms operative in the face of microorganismal invasion.

OVERVIEW OF THE SYSTEM

CN: Use red for L and light colors throughout. (1) Begin with the structures of the respiratory system. (2) Color the cross section of the trachea (D), including the respiratory mucosa (I). (3) Color the magnified section of the mucosa in the lowest view.

NASAL CAVITY_A
PHARYNX_B
LARYNX_C
TRACHEA_D
PRIMARY BRONCHI _E
BRONCHIAL TREE _F
R. LUNG_G L. LUNG _G'
DIAPHRAGM_H

The respiratory tract conducts air to the respiratory units of the lungs where it can readily be absorbed by the blood, and t removes carbon dioxide–laden air from the air cells and exhausts it to the external atmosphere. It develops and refines sounds into potentially intelligible vocalization, and it helps maintain the acid-base balance of the blood by blowing off excess acid in the form of carbon dioxide. Nowhere in the body does the outside world, with all its creatures of micro-scopic dimension, have such easy access to the protected interior cavities of the body as it does at the air/blood inter-faces of the lung. The respiratory tract has both air-conducting and respiratory (gas exchange) parts.

The air conduction tract includes an upper (*nasal cavity, pharynx, larynx*) and a lower tract (*trachea, primary bronchi and bronchial tree*). The upper tract is lined with respiratory mucosa, except in the lower pharynx where it has a stratified squamous epithelial surface. Except for the nose and pharynx, the skeleton of the respiratory tract is cartilaginous down to the smallest airways (bronchioles), where the cartilage is replaced by smooth muscle. The parts associated with gaseous exchange are the smallest bronchioles and alveoli (respiratory units), which take up much of the *lung's* volume.

The muscular diaphragm provides much of the force neces-ary for inspiration and expiration of air. One-quarter of that orce is generated by the intercostal muscles moving the ribs.

RESPIRATORY MUCOSA _I
PSEUDOSTRATIFIED
COLUMNAR EPITHELIUM_J
LAMINA PROPRIA_K
BLOOD VESSEL _L
GLAND_M

he mucosa of the respiratory tract is largely *pseudostratified columnar* and (in the bronchioles) cuboidal *epithelia* with mucus-secreting *goblet* (unicellular gland) *cells* and *cilia*. Here excreted mucus traps foreign particulate matter, inhaled air is hydrated (mixed with water), putting oxygen in solution, and the air is heated from underlying vessels. The epithelial cells re supported by a loose fibrous, *glandular, vascular lamina propria*, replete with fibroblasts and cells of the lymphoid system. Deep to this connective tissue layer is the supporting issue (bone in the nasal cavity, muscle in the pharynx, hyaline artilage in the trachea, larynx, and bronchi, smooth muscle in he bronchioles, and thin fibers supporting the air cells).

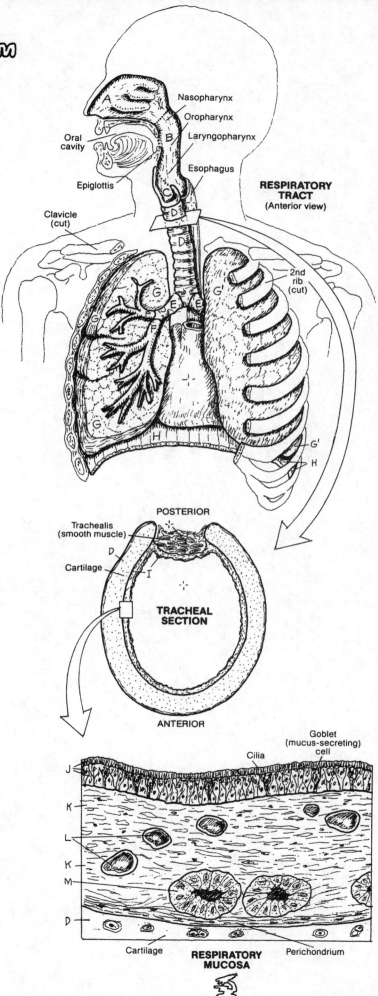

Nasopharynx

Oropharynx

Laryngopharynx

Esophagus

Oral cavity

Epiglottis

Clavicle (cut)

RESPIRATORY TRACT (Anterior view)

2nd rib (cut)

G'

H

POSTERIOR

Trachealis (smooth muscle)

Cartilage

TRACHEAL SECTION

ANTERIOR

Goblet (mucus-secreting) cell

Cilia

Cartilage

Perichondrium

RESPIRATORY MUCOSA

EXTERNAL NOSE, NASAL SEPTUM & NASAL CAVITY

CN: Use very light colors for H and I. (1) Begin with the upper illustration. (2) Color the nasal septum and its structure in the nasal cavities diagram. (3) Color the elements of the lateral wall of the nasal cavity and relations in the lowest illustration.

EXTERNAL NOSE
NASAL BONE A
CARTILAGE OF NASAL SEPTUM B
LATERAL NASAL CARTILAGE C
ALAR CARTILAGE D
FIBRO-FATTY TISSUE E

NASAL SEPTUM
CARTILAGE OF NASAL SEPTUM B
ALAR CARTILAGE D
PERPENDICULAR PLATE OF ETHMOID BONE F
VOMER BONE G

NASAL CAVITY & RELATIONS
NASAL BONE A
FRONTAL BONE H
SPHENOID BONE I
CRIBRIFORM PLATE OF ETHMOID F'
VESTIBULE OF NOSE D'
SUPERIOR CONCHA J
MIDDLE CONCHA K
INFERIOR CONCHA L
HARD PALATE M
SOFT PALATE N
LATERAL WALL O*

The nose is a largely cartilaginous affair external to the skull proper. Its orifices (nares, or nostrils) open into the nasal cavity of the skull, which is a bony tunnel divided by a partly cartilaginous *nasal septum*. The nasal cavity opens into the muscular pharynx through two bony-walled posterior apertures called choanae. The nose, situated as it is in front of the face, often receives the brunt of a facial impact. In such an event, it is not unusual for the *cartilage of the nasal septum* (septal cartilage) to break off from the *perpendicular plate of the ethmoid* This "deviated septum" may obstruct air flow through the narrowed half of the cavity. The skin-lined *vestibule* of the nose has long hairs (vibrissae) that serve to discourage entrance of foreign bodies. The nasal cavity is carpeted with a mucosal lining characterized by ciliated epithelial cells that secrete mucus and whose cilia sweep small particulate matter down into the nasopharynx. The bony *conchae* (so called because of their resemblance, in frontal section, to the conch shell) increase the surface area of the nasal cavity, significantly boosting the local temperature and moisture content. The *inferior concha* on each side is attached to the ethmoid bone by an immovable joint (suture); the *superior and middle conchae* are part of the ethmoid bone. The spaces under the conchae (meatuses) are open to paranasal sinuses (air-filled cavities), the subject of the next plate. Note that the roof of the nasal cavity (*cribriform plate*) transmits the olfactory nerve fibers; resting on or near this plate are the frontal lobes of the brain. Note that the floor of the nasal cavity is the *palate*, which is also the roof of the oral cavity. The *soft palate* is a muscular extension of the bony palate and plays a role in swallowing.

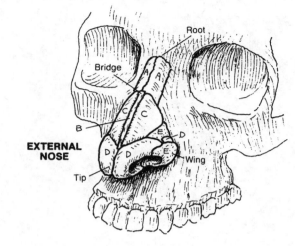

EXTERNAL NOSE

Root
Bridge
Wing
Tip

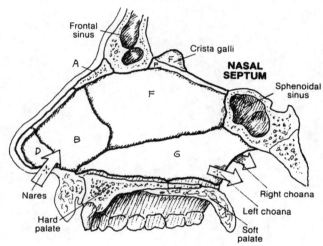

Frontal sinus
Crista galli
NASAL SEPTUM
Sphenoidal sinus
Nares
Right choana
Left choana
Hard palate
Soft palate

NASAL CAVITIES
(Diagrammatic)

Posterior
Roof
Right wall
Left wall
Floor
Anterior

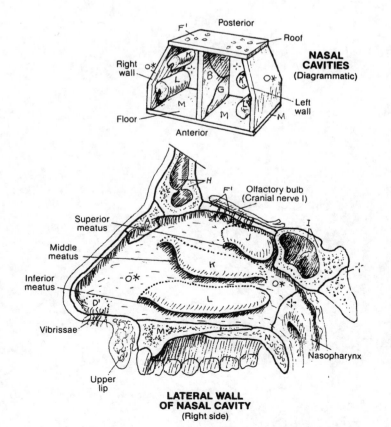

Olfactory bulb (Cranial nerve I)
Superior meatus
Middle meatus
Inferior meatus
Vibrissae
Nasopharynx
Upper lip

LATERAL WALL OF NASAL CAVITY
(Right side)

PARANASAL AIR SINUSES

CN: Use the same colors for the bones A and B, and conchae F, G, and H, that were used for those structures on Plate 130. (1) Color the sinus drainage sites in the lateral wall of the nasal cavity. Include the edges of the conchae which have been cut away to reveal the meatuses and related drainage sites. (2) Color the coronal section. Note that it is a composite view, showing openings into the nasal cavity that do not appear in any one single coronal plane. Even so, this view cannot show the relations of the sphenoid sinus and opening, nor the mastoid air cells and the auditory tube. (3) Color the lower drawings. Note that nasolacrimal duct and the duct of the frontal sinus are shown on one side only.

AIR SINUSES:
FRONTAL A
SPHENOID B
ETHMOID C
MAXILLARY D
MASTOID E

NASAL CONCHAE:
SUPERIOR F
MIDDLE G
INFERIOR H

OPENING OF AUDITORY TUBE I
NASOLACRIMAL DUCT J
NASAL SEPTUM K
NASAL CAVITY L*

The skull has a number of cavities in it. You are familiar with some of them (mouth, nose, external ear, orbits), but perhaps not so familiar with others. The frontal, sphenoid, maxillary, ethmoid, and temporal bones have variably sized cavities, all of which directly or indirectly communicate with the nasal cavity. These are the *paranasal air sinuses*, to be distinguished from the venous sinuses of the dura mater. These air sinuses serve to lighten the skull and they add timbre to the voice. They are lined with respiratory-type epithelium, which is continuous with the epithelium of the nasal cavity. The mucus secretions from these epithelial linings pass down canals and enter the nasal cavity just under the conchae (meatuses). Their specific drainage sites are indicated by the arrows. Should these passageways become blocked by inflammation and swelling, pressure builds within the sinuses to a point where considerable pain can be experienced (sinusitis, sinus headache). Agents that constrict the blood vessels (decongestants) help to reduce the swelling and reestablish proper drainage. The *mastoid air cells*, in the mastoid process of the temporal bone, drain into the middle ear (tympanic) cavity, communicating by way of the auditory (pharyngotympanic) tube with the nasopharynx just posterior to the nasal cavity. The *nasolacrimal duct* receives secretions from the lacrimal gland, which functions to keep the covering (conjunctiva) of the eye globe moist. Tears drain into slits at the medial aspect of the eyelids, which open into sacs that narrow into the nasolacrimal ducts. These ducts pass downward along the lateral walls of the nasal cavity and open into the meatus of the inferior concha on each side—and that is why one blows one's nose after crying.

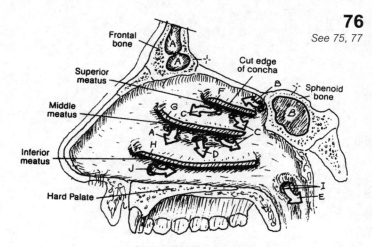

SINUS DRAINAGE SITES
(Right lateral wall of nasal cavity, nasal conchae removed)

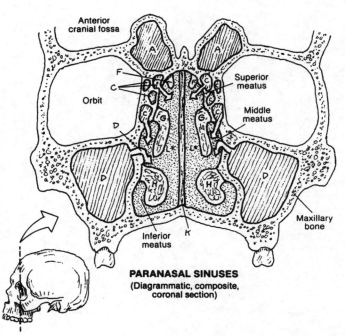

PARANASAL SINUSES
(Diagrammatic, composite, coronal section)

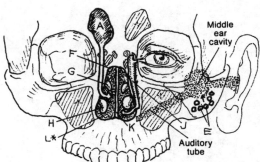

PARANASAL SINUS AND DUCTS

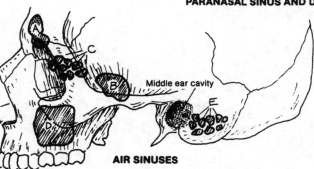

AIR SINUSES

PHARYNX & LARYNX

CN: Use dark or bright colors for N, O, and Q. (1) Begin with the overview diagram in the upper right corner. (2) Complete the large composite sagittal section (do not color the arrows representing air flow). Take note of the surrounding structure as a frame of reference (not to be colored). (3) Color all six laryngeal views simultaneously.

PHARYNX A
NASOPHARYNX B
PHARYNGEAL TONSIL C
OROPHARYNX D
PALATINE TONSIL E
LARYNGOPHARYNX F

The pharynx is an incomplete tube of mostly skeletal (constrictor) muscle and fibrous tissue, appearing to hang from the edges of the choanae (posterior nasal apertures) at the base of the skull. Posteriorly, it is supported by fascia in front of the sphenoid bone and the upper six cervical vertebrae. It is the posterior and inferior continuation of the *nasal cavity*; it is open to the *oral cavity* anteriorly. Inferiorly, it continues as the *esophagus* behind and the *larynx* in front. Most of pharynx is lined with stratified squamous epithelium, except the nasopharynx (respiratory lining). Coordinated muscular activity in the pharynx underlies the mechanism of swallowing (deglutition).

Masses of partially encapsulated lymphoid tissue incompletely encircle the nasal and oral openings into the pharynx (Waldeyer's ring)—i.e., at the opening of the auditory tube (tubal tonsils), at the roof of the nasopharynx (adenoids), between the palatoglossal and palatopharyngeal pillars (palatine tonsils; see Plate 137), and at the posterior tongue (lingual tonsils). See tonsil function in Plate 127.

HYOID BONE G
LARYNX H
LARYNGEAL CAVITY H'
EPIGLOTTIS I
THYROID CARTILAGE J
THYROHYOID MEMBRANE K
CRICOID CARTILAGE L
CRICOTHYROID LIGAMENT M
ARYTENOID CARTILAGE N
CORNICULATE CARTILAGE O
VESTIBULAR FOLD P
VOCAL FOLD Q
RIMA GLOTTIS R*

The larynx provides a mechanism for sound production, manipulation of sound waves, and protection from inadvertent aspiration (inhaling) of solid matter. The larynx is supported by a framework of hyaline cartilage connected by ligaments. Although associated with the larynx, the hyoid bone is not a laryngeal structure.

The thyroid cartilage is composed of two laminae that together are V-shaped when seen from above. The *arytenoid cartilages* articulate with the top of the cricoid, pivoting on it. The *vocal folds* are mucosa-lined ligaments stretching between thyroid and arytenoid cartilages. They are abducted/adducted by the movement of the arytenoid cartilages. In breathing they are abducted; in coughing, they are momentarily fully adducted (closing the *rima*), permitting intrathoracic pressure to build; opened rapidly by abduction of the folds, the rima experiences hurricane-force winds from the depths of the respiratory airway (explosive cough). During phonation, the vocal folds are generally adducted, varying somewhat with pitch and volume. The *vestibular folds* (false vocal folds) are fibrous and move only passively.

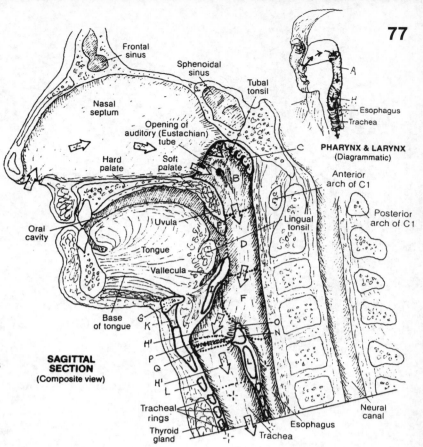

SAGITTAL SECTION (Composite view)

PHARYNX & LARYNX (Diagrammatic)

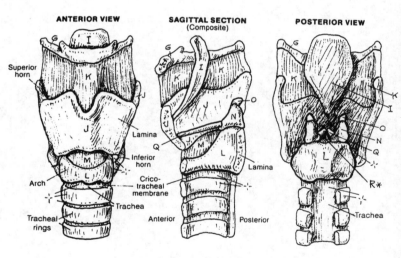

ANTERIOR VIEW

SAGITTAL SECTION (Composite)

POSTERIOR VIEW

VIEWS OF THE LARYNX

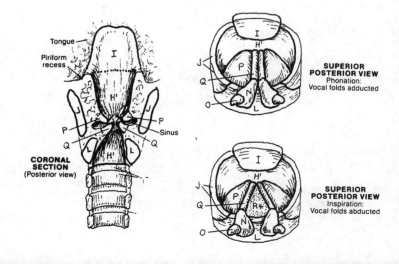

CORONAL SECTION (Posterior view)

SUPERIOR POSTERIOR VIEW Phonation: Vocal folds adducted

SUPERIOR POSTERIOR VIEW Inspiration: Vocal folds abducted

LOBES & PLEURAE OF THE LUNGS

CN: Use bright colors for A–E, very light colors for F and G, and a reddish-brown color for H. In all of the illustrations the thickness of the pleurae (F and G) has been enlarged for coloring purposes. (1) Begin with the anterior view. Note that the ribs and intercostal muscles have been removed (see Plate 50). Sections of the pleurae have been stripped away and separated. The potential pleural space is between these layers; in the coronal and cross sections, this space is drawn as a dark line and not as a structure to be colored. Similarly, the title is left uncolored. A small section of the parietal pleura has been cut and pulled away to reveal the underlying visceral pleura and a portion of the costodiaphragmatic recess below the lung superficial to the diaphragm. (2) Color the coronal view, noting the left crus of the diaphragm and the cardiac notch of the left lung. (3) Color the cross section of the lung lobes and pleurae (as seen from above), noting the vertebral level and the roots of the lungs.

LOBES :-

R. UPPER A   L. UPPER D
R. MIDDLE B   L. LOWER E
R. LOWER C

PLEURAE :-

VISCERAL PLEURA F
PLEURAL SPACE :-
PARIETAL PLEURA G

DIAPHRAGM H

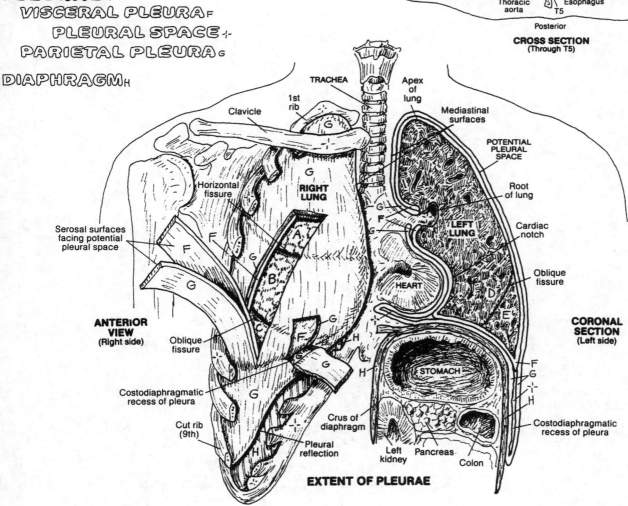

CROSS SECTION
(Through T5)

ANTERIOR VIEW
(Right side)

CORONAL SECTION
(Left side)

EXTENT OF PLEURAE

The lobes of the lungs are largely enveloped in *visceral pleura,* a thin serosal membrane that turns (reflects) off the lungs at their roots to become the *parietal pleura,* which lines the inner surface of the chest wall, the lateral mediastinum, and much of the diaphragm. These serous membranes are in contact with each other, separated by a thin layer of serous (watery, glycoprotein) fluid. The interface of these membranes is potentially a cavity or space (*pleural space/cavity*). With certain diseases, the space is capable of expanding to accommodate increasing amounts of fluid (pleural effusion) at the expense of the lung, resulting in a

reduction of total lung capacity. The serous fluid maintains surface tension between the pleural surfaces (resisting separation of visceral and parietal layers in contact with one another) and prevents frictional irritation between moving pleural membranes. During quiet inhalation, the inferior and anterior margins of the visceral pleura–lined lungs do not quite reach the parietal pleura, leaving a narrow space or recess—i.e., the costomediastinal recess between the rib cage and the mediastinum (not shown), and the costodiaphragmatic recess between rib cage and diaphragm (see coronal section at lower right).

LOWER RESPIRATORY TRACT

TRACHEA MAIN (PRIMARY) BRONCHUS LOBAR (SEC.) BRONCHUS
SEGMENTAL (TERTIARY) BRONCHI / BRONCHOPULMONARY SEGMENTS
1 APICAL 2 POST. 3 ANT. 4 LAT.(R.L.) 4 SUP.(L.L.)
5 MED.(R.L.) 5 INF.(L.L.) 6 SUP. 7 MED. BASAL
8 ANT. BASAL 9 LAT. BASAL 10 POST. BASAL

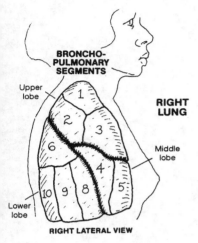

BRONCHO-PULMONARY SEGMENTS

RIGHT LUNG

Upper lobe

Middle lobe

Lower lobe

RIGHT LATERAL VIEW

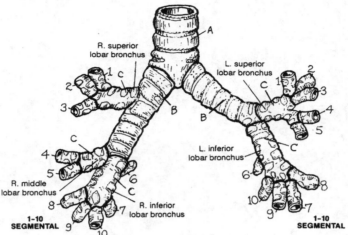

A

R. superior lobar bronchus

L. superior lobar bronchus

B

B

C

C

L. inferior lobar bronchus

R. middle lobar bronchus

C

R. inferior lobar bronchus

1-10 SEGMENTAL

1-10 SEGMENTAL

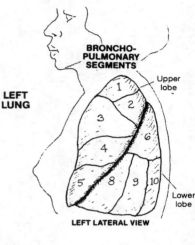

BRONCHO-PULMONARY SEGMENTS

LEFT LUNG

Upper lobe

Lower lobe

LEFT LATERAL VIEW

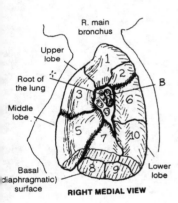

R. main bronchus

Upper lobe

Root of the lung

Middle lobe

B

Basal (diaphragmatic) surface

Lower lobe

RIGHT MEDIAL VIEW

CN: Save blue for H, purple for I, and red for J (in the respiratory unit below). (1) Use ten different colors for both lungs, and key those colors to the ten segmental bronchi of each lung. (2) Below, use the same color as above for the 7th segmental bronchus. Use one light color for the alveoli (G^1) and the alveolar sacs (G). Note in the gas exchange diagram that red blood cells in the purple capillary (F) receive three different colors according to their stage of oxygenation.

The lower respiratory tract consists of the *trachea* and the *bronchial tree*, including the respiratory units that are engaged in gaseous exchange. The lungs are divided by connective tissue septa into triangular-shaped, surgically resectable anatomical and functional units called *bronchopulmonary segments*, each served by a segmental bronchus, supplied by a segmental artery, and drained by segmental veins and lymphatics. Segments are of special significance to those interpreting lung sounds by stethoscope (auscultation) or listening to the sounds coming from the lungs when the chest wall is tapped (percussion). By such methods, sites of alveolar dysfunction/disease and levels of abnormal accumulations often can be determined.

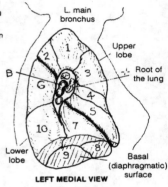

L. main bronchus

Upper lobe

Root of the lung

B

Lower lobe

Basal (diaphragmatic) surface

LEFT MEDIAL VIEW

BRONCHIOLE D
RESPIRATORY BRONCHIOLE E
ALVEOLAR DUCT F
ALVEOLAR SAC G & ALVEOLUS G'
PULMONARY ARTERIOLE H
CAPILLARY NETWORK I
####### PULMONARY VENULE J

Within each bronchopulmonary segment, a segmental bronchus branches into several *bronchioles* (less than 1 mm in diameter, supported by smooth muscle instead of cartilage). These bronchioles give off smaller terminal bronchioles, characterized by ciliated cuboidal cells without glands. The terminal bronchioles represent the end of the air-conducting pathway. Each terminal bronchiole divides into two or more *respiratory bronchioles*, characterized by occasional alveolar sacs on their walls. Each respiratory bronchiole supplies a respiratory unit, which is a discrete group of air cells (*alveoli*), arranged in *alveolar sacs*, fed by *alveolar ducts*. Extending from its source bronchiole, each respiratory bronchiole has more and more alveolar sacs, terminating as an alveolar duct opening into alveolar sacs. The walls of the air cells, composed of simple squamous epithelia supported by thin interwoven layers of elastic and reticular fibers, are surrounded by capillaries that arise from pulmonary arterioles and become the tributaries of pulmonary venules. The walls of these capillaries are fused to and structurally similar to those of the alveoli. Oxygen and carbon dioxide rapidly diffuse, on the basis of pressure gradients, through these walls.

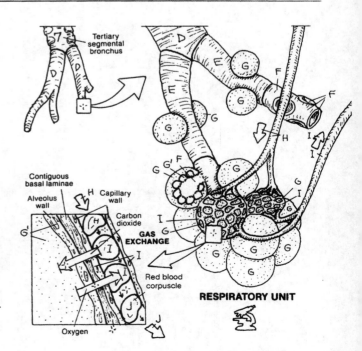

Tertiary segmental bronchus

Contiguous basal laminae

Capillary wall

Alveolus wall

Carbon dioxide

GAS EXCHANGE

Red blood corpuscle

Oxygen

RESPIRATORY UNIT

MECHANISM OF RESPIRATION

CN: Use light colors throughout, except for a bright or dark color for E. (1) Begin with the illustration at far left (inspiration); note that the thoracic wall (A) is shown only in the far right diagram. Color the diaphragm, its location represented by broken lines. (2) Color the expiration illustration and the bucket handle analogy. (3) Finish with the illustration at far right.

THORACIC WALL A
   RIB & COSTAL CARTILAGE B
   STERNUM C
   THORACIC VERTEBRAE D

MUSCLES OF INSPIRATION -:-
   DIAPHRAGM E
   EXTERNAL INTERCOSTAL F

MUSCLE OF EXPIRATION -:-
   INTERNAL INTERCOSTAL G

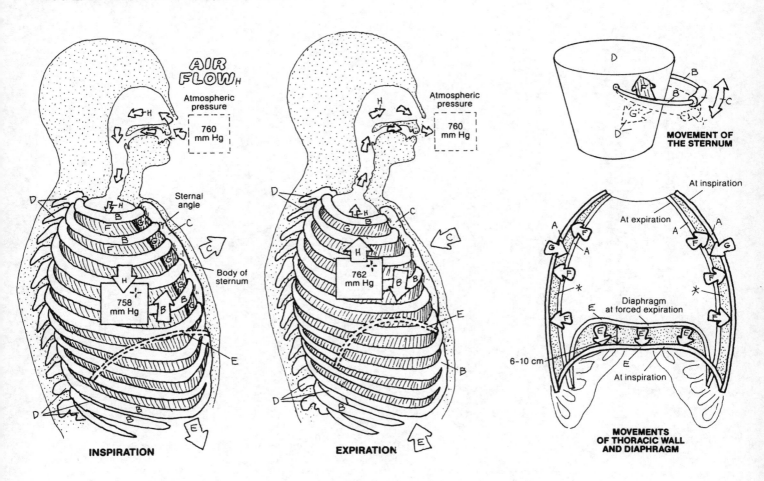

INSPIRATION

EXPIRATION

MOVEMENT OF THE STERNUM

MOVEMENTS OF THORACIC WALL AND DIAPHRAGM

The mechanism of respiration makes possible breathing, which consists of inhalation (inspiration) and exhalation (expiration) phases. The physical principle underlying air movement in/out of the thorax is the inverse relationship of pressure and volume (as one goes up, the other goes down). Volume changes within the *thorax* alter the intrathoracic pressure 1–2 mm Hg above/below atmospheric pressure (outside the body) in quiet breathing—enough of a change to move about 500 ml of air with each breath. The thoracic *diaphragm* accomplishes about 75% of the inspiratory effort, the *external intercostals* 25%. Expiration is largely diaphragm and external intercostal relaxation/stretch, and lung elasticity, with some help from the *internal intercostals*. In inspiration, contraction of the diaphragm flattens the muscle and lowers the floor of the thorax, increasing the vertical dimension of the thoracic cavity. Contraction of the external intercostals

elevates the ribs, swinging the sternal body slightly outward at the sternal angle. This increases the transverse and anteroposterior dimensions of the thoracic cavity. These actions collectively increase the intrathoracic volume, momentarily lowering the pressure within. Given the relatively higher atmospheric pressure outside the head, *air* is induced to enter the respiratory tract to find lower pressure. The action of the bucket handle demonstrates the hinge action at the sternal angle and related rib elevation. In expiration, the relaxed diaphragm forms "domes" over the underlying liver and stomach, decreasing the vertical dimension of the thorax. Recoil/descent of the ribs decreases the transverse and anteroposterior dimensions. The thoracic volume is thus decreased, momentarily increasing the intrathoracic pressure above atmospheric. *Air* escapes to the outside, aided by the natural elastic recoil of the lungs.

OVERVIEW

CN: When coloring the organs that overlap each other, use your lightest colors for D, E, T, V, and W. Each overlapping portion receives the color of both structures. (1) After coloring the alimentary canal, review the structures before completing the accessory organs. The central section of the transverse colon (J) has been removed to show deeper structures.

ALIMENTARY CANAL -:-
ORAL CAVITY A
PHARYNX B
ESOPHAGUS C
STOMACH D
SMALL INTESTINE -:-
DUODENUM E
JEJUNUM F
ILEUM G
LARGE INTESTINE -:-
CECUM H
VERMIFORM APPENDIX H'
COLON -:-
ASCENDING COLON I
TRANSVERSE COLON J
DESCENDING COLON K
SIGMOID COLON L
RECTUM M
ANAL CANAL N

ACCESSORY ORGANS -:-
TEETH O
TONGUE P
SALIVARY GLANDS -:-
SUBLINGUAL Q
SUBMANDIBULAR R
PAROTID S
LIVER T
GALL BLADDER U
BILE DUCT V
PANCREAS W

The digestive system consists of an alimentary canal with accessory organs. The canal begins with the *oral cavity*. Here the *teeth* pulverize ingested food while it is softened and partly digested by *salivary gland* secretions. The *tongue* aids in mechanical manipulation of the food and literally flips the food into the fibromuscular *pharynx* during swallowing.

The esophagus moves the bolus along to the *stomach* by peristaltic muscular contractions. Here the bolus is treated to mechanical and chemical digestion, then passed into the highly coiled *small intestine* for more enzymatic and mechanical digestive processes. Bile, produced by the *liver* and stored in the *gall bladder*, is discharged into the *duodenum* by a *bile duct*. Bile assists in the breakdown of fats. Digestive enzymes from the *pancreas* enter the duodenum as well. Nutrients of molecular size are extracted primarily from the lumen of the small intestine, absorbed by lining cells, and transferred to blood and lymph capillaries for eventual delivery to the liver for processing. The large intestine is concerned with absorption of minerals and water (proximal half) and storage. Undigested, unabsorbed material continues to the rectum for discharge through the anal canal and anus.

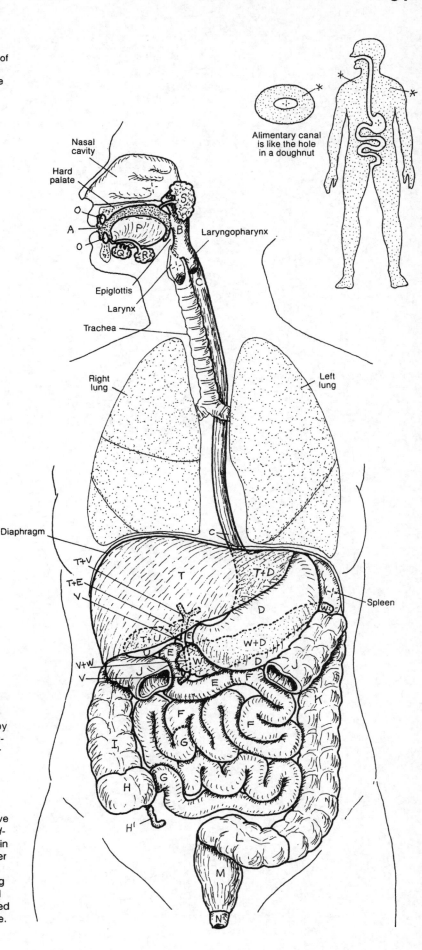

Nasal cavity

Hard palate

Laryngopharynx

Epiglottis

Larynx

Trachea

Right lung

Left lung

Diaphragm

Spleen

Alimentary canal is like the hole in a doughnut

KIDNEYS & RELATED RETROPERITONEAL STRUCTURES

CN: Use red for B, blue for L, and a very light color for X (use a color, not gray). (1) Color the various structures in the abdominal cavity. Part of the peritoneum (X), whose title is among the upper diagrams, is shown covering much of the right side. (2) At the upper right, note the relationship of the retroperitoneum to the parietal peritoneum.

KIDNEY A
URETER A'
URINARY BLADDER A²

AORTA B & BRANCHES :-
CELIAC A. & BRANCHES c
SUPRARENAL A. D
SUP. MESENTERIC A. E
RENAL A. F
TESTICULAR A. G
INF. MESENTERIC A. H
COMMON ILIAC A. I
INTERNAL ILIAC A. J
EXTERNAL ILIAC A. K

INFERIOR VENA CAVA L
& TRIBUTARIES :-
INTERNAL ILIAC V. M
EXTERNAL ILIAC V. N
COMMON ILIAC V. O
TESTICULAR V. P
RENAL V. Q
SUPRARENAL V. R
HEPATIC VS. S

ORGANS & DUCTS :-
ESOPHAGUS T
SUPRARENAL GLAND U
RECTUM V
DUCTUS (VAS) DEFERENS W

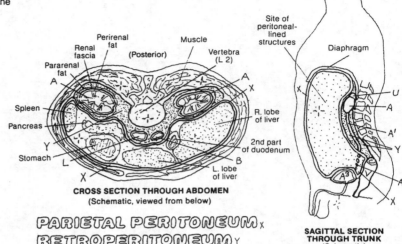

Site of peritoneal-lined structures

Perirenal fat

Renal fascia

Pararenal fat

Muscle

Vertebra (L 2)

(Posterior)

Spleen

Pancreas

Stomach

R. lobe of liver

2nd part of duodenum

L. lobe of liver

Diaphragm

CROSS SECTION THROUGH ABDOMEN
(Schematic, viewed from below)

PARIETAL PERITONEUM x
RETROPERITONEUM y

SAGITTAL SECTION THROUGH TRUNK
(Schematic)

The paired kidneys and ureters lie posterior to the *parietal peritoneum* of the abdominal cavity; they are, therefore, in the *retroperitoneum*. During fetal development, some abdominal structures arise in the retroperitoneum (e.g., kidneys), and some become retroperitoneal as a result of movement of visceral organs (e.g., ascending/descending colon, pancreas). The abdominal *aorta and its immediate branches* and the *inferior vena cava and its immediate tributaries* all are retroperitoneal. Arteries and veins travel between layers of peritoneum to reach the organs they supply/drain. Lymph nodes, lumbar trunks, and the cysternal chyli (not shown) all are retroperitoneal. The ureters descend in the retroperitoneum and under the parietal peritoneum to reach the posterior and inferior aspect of the bladder. Pelvic viscera and vessels lie deep to the parietal peritoneum.

The kidneys are encapsulated in perirenal fat, secured by an outer, stronger layer (renal fascia). Each kidney and its fascia are packed in pararenal fat. These compartments do not communicate between left and right. Such a support system permits kidney movement during respiration but secures them against impact forces.

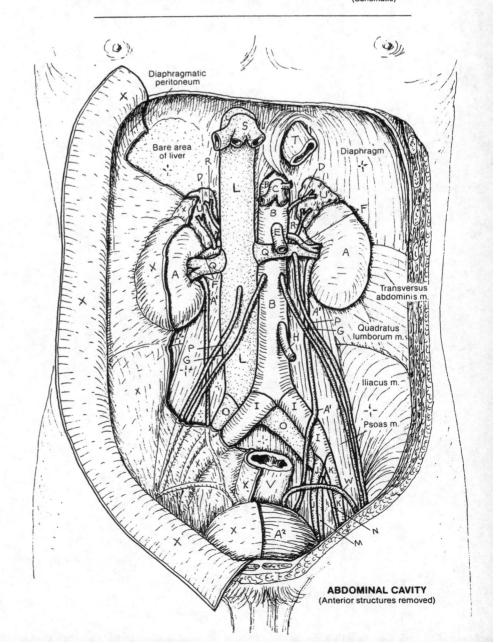

Diaphragmatic peritoneum

Bare area of liver

Diaphragm

Transversus abdominis m.

Quadratus lumborum m.

Iliacus m.

Psoas m.

ABDOMINAL CAVITY
(Anterior structures removed)

INTRODUCTION

C, I: Use a very light color for C and a darker one for D (actually located on posterior surface of thyroid). (1) After coloring endocrine glands and tissues, color the scheme at lower left.

ENDOCRINE GLANDS:
    HYPOPHYSIS (PITUITARY) A
    PINEAL B
    THYROID C
    PARATHYROID (4) D
    THYMUS E
    ADRENAL (SUPRARENAL) (2) F
    PANCREAS G
    OVARY (2) H
    TESTIS (2) I

ENDOCRINE TISSUES:
    HYPOTHALAMUS J
    HEART (ATRIA) K
    KIDNEY (2) L
    GASTROINTESTINAL TRACT M
    PLACENTA N

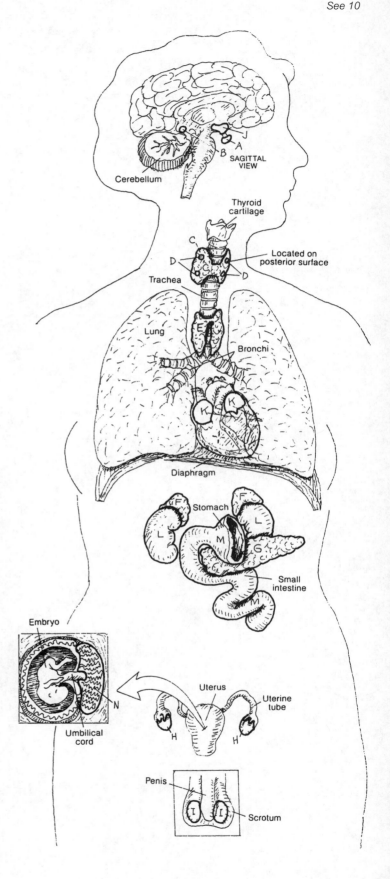

Endocrine glands and tissues are discrete masses of secretory cells and their supporting tissues in close proximity to blood capillaries, into which the cells secrete their hormones. The glands and tissues are ductless. Hormones are chemical agents usually effective among cells (target organs) located some distance from their source. Hormonal secretion results in negative or positive feedback control mechanisms. In the broader scope, hormonal activity results in growth, reproduction, and related activity as well as metabolic stability in the internal environment. Stability of the internal environment is called homeostasis.

The classical endocrine glands listed and shown here are presented in the following plates, with the exception of the pineal gland (see Plate 75) and the thymus (see Plate 124). Also listed here are just a few of the myriad tissues/cells that secrete chemical agents influential in cellular activities. The role of the hypothalamus can be colored in Plates 152 and 153. The atria of the heart secrete atrial natriuretic peptide (ANP) during periods of weak myocardial contraction, resulting in increased excretion of sodium and water. The juxtaglomerular cells of the kidney (Plate 150) secrete renin, an enzyme that converts angiotensinogen to angiotensin I and indirectly induces increased blood pressure and conservation of body fluids, such as during hemorrhage. Numerous endocrine factors secreted by cells of the gastrointestinal tract influence intestinal motility and enzyme secretion. The placenta secretes, among many hormones, human chorionic gonadotropin, which contributes to the support of embryonic growth during the first 90 days post-fertilization by stimulating the growth of the corpus luteum (Plates 161, 163, 165, 166).

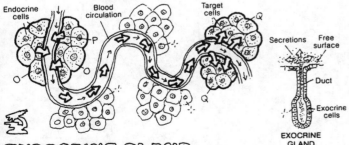

ENDOCRINE FUNCTION

ENDOCRINE GLAND O
HORMONAL SECRETION P
TARGET ORGAN Q

BIBLIOGRAPHY AND REFERENCES

Agur, A. (ed), *Grant's Atlas of Anatomy*, 10th ed., Williams & Wilkins, Baltimore, 1999

Alcamo, I. Edw., L.M. Elson, *The Microbiology Coloring Book*, HarperCollins, New York, 1996

Basmajian, J., *Muscles Alive*, 5th ed., Williams & Wilkins, Baltimore, 1985

Bergman, R. S. Thompson, A. Affifi, F. Saadeh, *Compendium of Human Anatomic Variation*, Urban and Schwarzenberg, Baltimore, 1988

Dawson, D., M. Mallett, L. Millender, *Entrapment Neuropathies*, 2nd ed., Little Brown and Co., Boston, 1990

Diamond, M.C., A.B. Scheibel, L.M. Elson, *The Human Brain Coloring Book*, HarperCollins, New York, 1985.

DuBrul, L., *Sicher's Oral Anatomy*, 7th ed., C.V. Mosby, St. Louis, 1980

Guyton, A.C., J.E. Hall, *Textbook of Medical Physiology*, 10th ed., W.B. Saunders, Philadelphia, 2000

Haymaker, W., B. Woodhall, *Peripheral Nerve Injuries: Principles of Diagnosis*, 2nd ed., W.B. Saunders, Philadelphia, 1953

Hoppenfeld, S. *Physical Examination of the Spine and Extremities*, Appleton-Century-Crofts, New York, 1976.

Junqueira, L.C., J. Carneiro, R. Kelley, *Basic Histology*, 9th ed., Appleton & Lange, Connecticut, 1998

Kapit, W., R. Macey, E. Meisami, *The Physiology Coloring Book*, Benjamin Cummings, San Francisco, 2000

Levinson, W., E. Jawetz, *Medical Microbiology & Immunology*, Lange Medical Books/McGraw-Hill, New York 2000

Lockhart, R.D., G.F. Hamilton, F.W. Fyfe, *Anatomy of the Human Body*, 2nd ed., J.B. Lippincott Co., Philadelphia, 1959

Marieb, E.N., J. Mallatt, *Human Anatomy*, 3rd ed., Benjamin Cummings, San Francisco, 2001

Moore, K. *The Developing Human: Clinically Oriented Embryology*, 6th ed., W.B. Saunders, Philadelphia, 1998

Netter, F., S. Colacino (ed.), *Atlas of Human Anatomy*, Ciba-Geigy Corp., Summit, N.J., 1998

_____, *Nomina Anatomica*, 6th edition, Churchill Livingstone, New York, 1989

Roberts, M., J. Hanaway, *Atlas of the Human Brain in Section*, 2nd ed., Lea and Febiger, Philadelphia, 1986

Rothman, S., W. Glenn, *Multiplanar CT of the Spine*, University Park Press, Baltimore, 1985

Skinner, H., *The Origin of Medical Terms*, 2nd ed., Williams & Wilkins, Baltimore, 1961

Warfel, J., *The Head, Neck, and Trunk: Muscles and Motor Points*, 6th ed., Lea and Febiger, Philadelphia, 1993

Warfel, J., *The Extremities*, 6th ed., Lea and Febiger, Philadelphia, 1993

White, A., M. Panjabi, *Clinical Biomechanics of the Spine*, 2nd ed., J.B. Lippincott, Philadelphia, 1990.

Williams, P.L. (ed.), *Gray's Anatomy*, 38th ed., Churchill Livingstone, New York, 1995

GLOSSARY

Anatomical terms as set forth and revised by the International Anatomical Nomenclature Committee of the International Congress of Anatomists, published in the 6th Edition of the *Nomina Anatomica* (1989), are included herein. For further inquiry, consult a standard medical dictionary. The terms here are compatible with those listed in *Dorland's Illustrated Medical Dictionary*, 27th Edition. Pronunciation of terms is given phonetically (as they sound, not by standard dictionary symbols). The primary accent (emphasis) is indicated by capitalized letters, e.g., ah-NAT-oh-mee, included with the definitions. The plural form is in parentheses following the term defined, e.g., alveolus(i) or alveoli. Pl. = plural.

A

A-, an-, without.

Ab-, away from the midline.

AB, antibody.

Abdomen, the region between the thoracic diaphragm and the pelvis.

Abscess (AB-sess), a cavity in disintegrating tissue, characterized by the presence of pus and infective agents.

Achilles, in Greek mythology, one of the sons of Peleus, a young king, and Thetis, one of the immortal goddesses of the sea. Not wanting Achilles to be mortal like his father, Thetis dipped him into the River Styx, holding him by the heel cord (tendocalcaneus), making him invulnerable to harm except at that spot. Achilles later became a great Greek warrior. In the many wars between Greece and Troy, Achilles was invulnerable to harm. At last, a Trojan, aided by the god Apollo, slew Achilles with an arrow into the vulnerable heel cord. The term "Achilles heel" refers to one's vulnerabilities; the Achilles tendon is the tendocalcaneus.

Acinus(i) (ASS-ee-nus), a saclike gland.

Actin, a protein of muscle, associated with the contraction/relaxation of muscle cells.

Ad-, toward the midline.

Adeno- (ADD-eh-no), gland.

Afferent, leading to a center.

Ag, antigen.

AIDS, acquired immunodeficiency syndrome.

-algia, pain.

Alimentary canal, the digestive tract from mouth to anus.

Alveolus(i) (al-VEE-oh-lus), grape-shaped cavity, rounded or oblong. Refers to the shape of exocrine glands, air spaces within the lungs, and the bony sockets for teeth.

Amino acid (ah-MEEN-oh), a two-carbon molecule with a side chain that contains either nitrogen (in the form of NH_2) or a carboxyl group (-COOH).

Amorphous (ay-MORF-us), without apparent structure at some given level of observation. What appears amorphous at 1000X magnification may be quite structured at 500,000X.

Amphi-, double, about, around, both sides.

Amphiarthrosis(es) (AM-fee-ar-THRO-sis), see joint classification, functional.

Ampulla(e), dilatation of a tubular structure.

Anastomosis(es) (ah-NASS-toh-moh-sis), connection between two vessels.

Anatomy (ah-NAT-oh-mee), *ana* = up, *tome* = to cut; the study of structure.

Anemia (ah-NEE-mee-ah), a condition of inadequate numbers of red blood corpuscles.

Angina (an-JYNE-ah), pain, especially cardiac pain.

Angio-, a vessel.

Angle, the point of junction of two intersecting lines, as in the inferior angle of the scapula between the vertebral (medial) and axillary (lateral) borders of that bone.

Angulus(i), an angle.

Ankle, the tarsus. The region between the leg and foot.

Annulus(i) (AN-new-lus), a ringlike or circular structure.

Ano-, anus.

Anomaly (ah-NOM-ah-lee), an abnormality, especially in relation to congenital or developmental variations from the normal.

A.N.S. or ANS, autonomic nervous system.

Ansa, loop.

Anserine, like a goose. *Pes anserinus*, goose foot.

Ante- (AN-tee), forward.

Antebrachium, forearm.

Antecubital, in front of the elbow (cubitus).

Anti-, against.

Antibody, a complex protein (immunoglobulin). A product of activated B lymphocytes and plasma cells, it is synthesized as part of an immune response to the presence of a specific antigen.

Antigen, any substance that is capable of inciting an immune response and reacting with the products of that response. Antigens may be in solution (toxins) or may be solid structures (microorganisms, cell fragments, and so on). Particulate matter that is phagocytosed but does not incite an immune response does not constitute antigen. Specific antibodies formed by cloning (monoclonal antibodies) may react with certain surface molecules on a cell membrane; those surface molecules constitute antigens.

Antigenic determinant, the specific part of an antigen that reacts with the product of an immune response (antibody, complement).

Aperture (AP-er-chur), an opening.

Apical, an apex or pointed extremity.

Aponeurosis(es), a flat tendon.

Apophyseal (app-oh-FIZZ-ee-al), refers to apophysis.

Apophysis(es) (ah-POFF-ee-sis), an outgrowth; a process.

Arborization (ar-bor-eye-ZAY-shun), branching of terminal dendrites.

GLOSSARY

Areolar (ah-REE-oh-lar), filled with spaces.

Arm, that part of the upper limb between the shoulder and elbow joints.

Arrhythmia(s) (a-RITH-mee-ah), a variation from the normal rhythm of the heartbeat; the absence of rhythm.

Arterio-, artery.

Arthr- (AR-thr), joint.

Arthritis(ides) (ar-THRI-tiss), inflammation of a joint.

Articular, joint.

Articular process, an outgrowth of bone on which there is a cartilaginous surface for articulation with another similar surface.

Articulation, a joint or connection of bones, movable or not; occlusion between teeth; enunciation of words.

Aspera, rough.

Aster, a ray, as in rays of light; in the cell, rays of microtubules projecting from centrioles.

Atherosclerosis, a form of arterioclerosis or hardening of the arteries; specifically, characterized by yellowish plaques of cholesterol and lipid in the tunica intima of medium and large arteries.

ATP, adenosine triphosphate, a nucleotide compound containing three high-energy phosphate bonds attached to a phosphate group; energy is released when the ATP is hydrolyzed to adenosine diphosphate and a phosphate group.

Atrophy (AT-troh-fee), usually associated with decrease in size, as in muscle atrophy.

Avascular (ay-VASS-kew-lur), without blood vessels or, in some cases, blood.

Avulsion, tearing a part away from the whole, as in tearing a tendon from its attachment to bone.

B

Back, the region making up the posteriormost wall of the thorax and abdomen, supported by the thoracic and lumbar vertebrae. Strictly defined, it excludes the neck and sacrum/coccyx (pelvis).

Basal lamina(e), a thin layer of interwoven collagen fibrils interfacing epithelial cells (and certain other nonepithelial cells) and connective tissue. Seen only with an electron microscope.

Basement membrane, basal lamina and a contiguous layer of collagenous tissue. Seen with a light microscope, it controls diffusion and transport into/out of the cell.

Basilar, at the base or bottom.

Benign, nonmalignant; often used to mean mild or of lesser significance.

Bi-, two.

Bicipital, two-headed.

Bicuspid, a structure, e.g., a tooth or valve, with two cusps.

Bifurcate (BY-fur-cate), to branch.

Bilateral, both sides (left and right).

-blast, formative cell; immature form.

Blephar-, eyelid.

Blood-borne, refers to some structure carried by the blood.

Blood–brain barrier, a state in the CNS in which substances toxic or harmful to the brain are physically prevented from getting to the brain; it is represented by tight endothelial junctions in capillaries of the brain, tight layers of pia mater around vessels, and the presence of neuroglial endfeet surrounding vessels.

Bolus, a mass of food; any discrete mass.

Bone, immature, see bone, woven.

Bone, lamellar, mature bone characterized by organized layers or lamellae of bone.

Bone, mature, see bone, lamellar.

Bone, primary, see bone, woven.

Bone, secondary, see bone, lamellar.

Bone, woven, immature bone characterized by random arrangements of collagen tissue and without the typical lamellar organization seen in more mature bone.

Brachi-, arm.

Bronch-, referring to bronchi or bronchioles of the respiratory tract.

Bursa(e), synovial-lined sac between tendons and bone or muscle and muscle, or any other site in which movement of structure tends to irritate or injure adjacent structure. It contains synovial fluid and is lined externally by fibrous connective tissue.

Bursitis, inflammation of a bursa.

C

CD4, CD, "clusters of differentiation." The abbreviation refers to a collection of cell surface molecules with specific structural characteristics (markers) reflecting a common lineage. The identification of these markers is made by purebred (monoclonal) antibodies, which react only with surface markers of cells of a common lineage. Cells exhibiting cell surface markers of a common lineage belong to a cluster (of differentiation), identified by number, e.g., 4. Most helper T lymphocytes have markers of three different clusters—CD3, CD4, and CD8. Cytotoxic T lymphocytes are CD3, CD4, and CD8.

Cadaver (ka-DA-ver), a dead body.

Canaliculus(i), a small canal.

Cancellous (KAN-sell-us), having a lattice-like or spongy structure with visible holes.

Cancer, a condition in which certain cells undergo uncontrolled mitoses with invasiveness and metastasis (migrating from the point of origin to other sites, usually by way of the lymphatic and/or blood vascular systems). There are two broad divisions: carcinoma, cancer of epithelial cells; sarcoma, cancer of the connective tissues.

Capillary attraction, the force that attracts fluid to a surface, such as water flowing along the undersurface of a pouring tube.

Capitulum, a rounded process of bone, usually covered with articular cartilage. Synonym: capitellum.

Caput medusae, the head of the mythical Medusa, whose golden hair entranced Neptune. The jealous Minerva turned the hair of Medusa into a mass of snakes. The term "caput medusae" is used for the snake-like appearance of the dilated, interwoven mass of subcutaneous veins surrounding the umbilicus in the condition of portal vein obstruction.

Cardio-, heart

Carpus, carpo-, wrist.

Cauda equina (horse's tail), the vertically oriented bundle of nerve roots within the vertebral canal below the level of the first lumbar vertebra (L1). Includes nerve roots for spinal nerves L2 through the Co2, bilaterally.

Cauda equina syndrome, irritation/compression of the cauda equina, resulting in bilateral symptoms and signs that may include bladder and bowel incontinence, weakness in the lower limb muscles, sensory impairment from the perineum to the toes, and reflex changes.

Cauterization, destruction of tissue by heat, as with an electrocauterizing instrument.

Cavity, potential, a space between membranes that can enlarge with fluid accumulation, as in the peritoneal cavity (ascites) or pericardial cavity (cardiac tamponade).

Cell body, the main, largest single mass of a neuron, containing the nucleus surrounded by organelles in the cytoplasm.

-centesis, puncture.

Central, at or toward the center.

Ceph-, head.

Cerebro-, brain; specifically, cerebral hemisphere.

Cerumen (sur-ROO-men), the wax secretion of the external ear.

Cerv-, neck.

Cheil- (KY-el), lip.

Chest, the thorax.

Chir- (kir), hand.

Choana(e) (KOH-ah-nah), referring to a funnel, as in the nasal passageways or apertures.

Chol- (koll), bile.

Chondro- (KOND-row), cartilage.

Chromosome (KRO-moh-sohm), "colored body."

Circulare(s), circle

-clast (klast), disruption, breaking up.

Clearing, the process of clearing water or solvent out of a specimen in preparation for microscopic study.

Cleavage, division into distinct parts.

Clinical, the setting in which a person is examined for evidence of injury or disease.

Clot, coagulated blood; a reticular framework of fibrin, platelets, and other blood cells. Associated fluid is serum.

cm, centimeter.

C.N.S. or CNS, central nervous system, consisting of the brain and spinal cord.

Co-, con-, together.

Coagulation, the clotting of the blood.

Coelom (SE-lom), the embryonic body cavity.

Collagen (KOLL-ah-jen), the protein of connective tissue fibers. Several different types are found in fasciae, tendons, ligaments, cartilage, bone, vessels, organs, scar tissue, and wherever support or binding is needed. Formed by fibroblasts, endothelia, muscle cells, and Schwann cells.

Collateral circulation, alternate circulatory routes; vessels between two or more points that exist in addition to the primary vessels between those points. Such circulation exists by virtue of anastamoses among a number of vessels.

Colli-, neck.

Colo-, colon.

Complement, a group of proteins in the blood whose activation causes their cleavage and fragmentation. The fragments have several biologic functions, of which one is combining with antibody/antigen complexes, enhancing the destruction of antigen.

Concentric contraction, a type of muscle contraction in which the internal contracting force of a muscle is greater than the external load imposed on it (positive work), so that the muscle shortens.

Conch (kawnk), a large spiral shell.

Concha(e) (KAWNK-ah, or KAWN-cha; pl. KAWNK-ee or KAWN-chee), a structure shaped like a conch shell.

Concretion, an inorganic or mineralized mass, usually in a cavity or tissue.

Condylar, condyloid, referring to a rounded process, as in a joint surface

Condyle, a rounded projection of bone; usually a joint surface, covered with articular cartilage.

Contiguous (kon-TIG-yu-us), adjoining and being in contact. The basement membrane is contiguous with the basal surfaces of certain epithelial cells.

Contra-, against.

Contraction, shortening.

Cornu(a) (KOR-new), a horn-shaped process.

Corona, crown.

Corona radiata, radiating crown. The term refers to the appearance of the subcortical white matter and, specifically, the projection system.

Coronoid (KOR-oh-noid), crownlike or beak-shaped; refers to a bony process.

Corpus(ora), body.

Corpuscle (KOR-pus-il), any small body, not necessarily a cell. Red blood corpuscles lack nuclei and are not considered cells.

Costa, rib

Costochondritis, an inflammation surrounding the cartilage of a joint of a rib, usually involving the synovium and fibrous joint capsule and perhaps related ligaments.

Coxa(e), hip; the hip (coxal) joint. Deformities of the upper femur often include the term (such as coxa varus or coxa valgus). Preceded by the term "os," it refers to the coxal or hip bone.

Crani-, cranium.

Cranium, that part of the skull containing the brain.

Cribriform, perforated; like a sieve.

-crine (krin), separate off, referring to glands that separate from classical epithelial surfaces.

Cruciate, shaped like a cross.

Crus (crura), leg.

Crux, cross.

Cu., cubic.

Cubital, front (anterior aspect) of the elbow.

Cusp, a triangular structure characterized by a tapering projection.

Cutan-, cutaneous (kew-TANE-ee-us), referring to the skin.

Cystitis, inflammation of the urinary bladder.

Cysto-, bladder.

GLOSSARY

-cyte (site), cell.

Cytokine, a product of a cell that facilitates destruction of antigen by inducing or enhancing an immune response.

Cytolysis, the dissolution and destruction of a cell.

Cytotoxin, a product of a cell that acts to destroy another cell or has a toxic effect.

D

Dachry-, relating to tears.

Dactyl, finger, toe.

Decussation, crossing over.

Defecation, elimination of waste material through the anal canal/anus from the rectum.

Deglutition, swallowing.

Demi-, half.

Denervation (dee-nerv-AY-shun), a condition in which a muscle or area of the body is isolated from its nerve supply.

Dentin (DEN-tin), the hard portion of a tooth. It is more dense (harder) than bone, less dense (softer) than enamel.

Depolarization, neutralization of a polarity; in biological systems, it is an electrical change in stimulated excitable tissues (nerves, specialized cardiac muscle cells) from a baseline polarity (about –90 millivolts) toward neutral (0 millivolts). Such an event induces the conduction of an electrochemical wave (impulse) to move along an excitable tissue (e.g., nerve).

Derm-, skin.

-desis, fixation.

Desiccation (dess-ee-KAY-shun), drying out; without water.

Desmo-, fibrous.

Dexterity, skill with the hands.

Di-, twice.

Diaphragm(ae) (DIE-ah-fram), a partition separating two cavities. There are three significant fibromuscular diaphragms in the body: thoracic (separating thorax and abdomen), pelvic (separating pelvis and perineum), and urogenital (separating the anterior recesses of the ischiorectal fossa from the superficial perineal space).

Diarthrosis(es) (die-ar-THRO-sis), see joint classification, functional.

Differentiation, making something different; in the development of a cell, it is the structural and functional changes within that cell that make it different from other cells; an increase in heterogeneity and diversification.

Diffusion, spontaneous movement of molecules without the application of additional forces.

Digit, finger or toe.

Diploic, referring to the marrow layer between the inner and outer layers of compact bone in the flat bones of the skull.

Dis-, apart.

Disc, a wafer-shaped, rounded or oval fibrocartilaginous structure; if crescent-shaped, it is called a meniscus. It may interface the articular cartilage surface in a synovial joint (articular disc) or it may interface opposing cartilage endplates of vertebral bodies (intervertebral disc).

Discharge, to set off or release, to fire, to let go.

Dissect (dis-SECT), to cut up, to take apart. In gross anatomy laboratories, the human body is studied by an ordered dissection by regions.

Dys-, abnormal, painful, or difficult.

Dorsum, back. Refers to the posterior aspect of the hand and the "top" of the foot.

E

Ec-, out.

Eccentric contraction, a type of muscle contraction wherein contracted muscle is stretched and lengthened during the contraction, such as antigravity contractions by antagonists during movement directed toward gravity. Even though there is a load on the muscle, the muscle is stretched (negative work).

-ectasis(es), dilatation.

-ectomy, removal.

Efferent, leading away from a center (organ or structure).

Elbow, the region between the arm and forearm.

Electrochemical, referring to combined properties of electrical and chemical, such as the neuronal impulse.

Ellipsoid, a closed curve more oval than a perfect circle. Ellipsoid joints are reduced forms of ball-and-socket joints; broadly speaking, they include condylar-shaped joints.

Em-, in.

Embalm (em-BAHM), to treat a dead body with preservative chemicals to prevent structural breakdown by microorganisms.

-emia, blood.

Emissary vein, a vein that drains a dural venous sinus and passes through the skull bone by way of a foramen.

Emission, an involuntary release of semen; also, the movement of sperm from the epididymis to the prostate during sexual stimulation in the male.

En-, in.

Encapsulate, to surround with a capsule.

Encephalo-, brain.

Endo-, in.

Endochondral (en-do-KON-dral), endo = in, chondral = cartilage.

Endochondral ossification, see ossification.

Endocrine (EN-do-krin), endo = in, crine = separate. Glands that secrete their products into the tissue fluids or vascular system.

Endocytosis, the ingestion of matter into a cell by surrounding the material with the cell membrane and budding it off in the cytoplasm.

Endometr-, endometrium.

Endosteum(a), the lining of the medullary canal of long bones, consisting of a thin sheet of collagen fibers and large numbers of osteoprogenitor cells.

Endothelium(a) (en-do-THEE-lee-um), the epithelial lining of blood and lymph vessels and the heart cavities. Endothelia are of mesenchymal origin, not

GLOSSARY

ectodermal, and have properties different from classical epithelia.

Entero-, referring to the intestines.

Enteroendocrine, refers to cells of the epithelial layer/ glands of the gastrointestinal mucosa, which secrete hormones that stimulate/inhibit (regulate) intestinal/ pancreatic gland secretion and/or motility of smooth muscle.

Enzyme, a protein molecule that facilitates a reaction without becoming involved (changed or destroyed) in the reaction. Enzymes are identified by the suffix *-ase*.

Epi-, upon, at.

Epicondyle, an elevation of bone above a condyle.

Epidid-, epididymis.

Epidural, outside the dura, between the dura and the skull.

Epithelium(a) (ep-ee-THEE-lee-um), *epi* = upon, *thelia* = nipple.

Erg, a unit of work.

Ergo-, a combining form meaning "work."

Ex-, exo-, out.

Excretion (ex-CREE-shun), the discharging of or elimination of materials, such as waste matter. If the material excreted has some useful in-body function or use outside the body (e.g., semen), it has probably been secreted, not excreted, although there is no universal agreement on this. See secretion.

Exocrine (EX-oh-krin), *exo* = out, *crine* = separate off; referring to glands that separate from classical epithelial surfaces.

Exocytosis, removal of matter from a cell.

Extracellular, outside of the cell, such as the fibrous tissue supporting cells, and vascular spaces.

Extrinsic, coming from the outside. With reference to a specific area (e.g., thumb, hand, foot), extrinsic muscles are those with origins outside of the specific area, but which insert in the area and have an effect on the specific area. See intrinsic.

F

Facet (FASS-et), a small plane or slightly concave surface. The flat cartilaginous surfaces of a joint may be called facets, as on the articular processes of vertebrae.

Facet joint, a joint between articular processes of adjacent vertebrae; also called *zygapophyseal joints*.

Facilitation, enhancement of or assistance in an event.

Falx inguinalis (conjoint tendon), a tendon composed of fibers from transversus abdominis and internal oblique that arcs over the spermatic cord and attaches to the pectineal line of the pubic bone. See Plate 51.

Fascia(e) (FASH-uh, pl. FASH-ee), a general term for a layer or layers of loose or dense, irregular, fibrous connective tissue. Superficial fascia, often infiltrated with adipose tissue, is just under the skin. Deep fascia envelops skeletal muscle and fills in spaces between superficial fascia and deeper structure, and between/among muscle bellies (myofascial structure). Extensions of deep fasciae form intermuscular

septa, support viscera (e.g., endopelvic fascia), act as fibrous bands, and support neurovascular bundles. Smaller, microscopic layers of fibrous tissue (e.g., perimysium, endomysium, vascular tunics) do not constitute deep fascia, even though they may be distant extensions of it. These fibrous connective tissue investments, integrated with tendons, ligaments, periosteum, and bone, blend into a unibody construction, resistant to all but the most traumatic of forces.

Fascia, thoracolumbar, strong layer enveloping the deep back or paravertebral muscles from the iliac crest and sacrum to the ribs/sternum. Plays an important role in limiting and moving motion segments of the back.

Fascicle(s) (FASS-ih-kul), a bundle.

Feedback, a communication relationship between two structures, e.g., wherein the output (secretion) of one substance induces an inhibition or facilitation of the secretion of another substance. Negative feedback reflects an inhibitory effect; positive feedback reflects a facilitating relationship.

Fibers, elongated lengths of tissue, e.g., living muscle fibers (cells or their parts), connective tissue fibers (nonliving cell products), living nerve fibers (extensions of cell bodies).

Fibril (FY-brill), en elongated structure smaller than and part of a fiber.

Fibrous (FY-brus), referring to a fiber or fiberlike quality.

Fibrosus (fy-BROHS-us), a fibrous stucture.

Filament, a small delicate fiber; in biology, a structure of some length, often smaller than a fibril, which is smaller than a fiber.

Filtration, movement of a fluid by the application of a force, such as pressure, vacuum, or gravity.

Fissure, a narrow crack or deep groove.

Fixation, a process in preparation of tissue for microscopic study. Treatment of fresh tissue with a fixative preserves structure, preventing autolysis and bacterial degradation.

Flaccid (FLA-sid or FLAK-sid), without tone; denervated; lax or soft.

Foot, the most distal part of the lower limb. The skeleton of the foot consists of the tarsus, metatarsal bones, and phalanges. It joins with the leg at the ankle (talotibiofibular joint).

Foramen(ina) (foh-RAY-men), opening or hole.

Forearm, that part of the upper limb between the elbow and wrist (radiocarpal) joints.

Forefoot, that part of the foot anterior to the transverse tarsal (talonavicular and calcaneocuboid) joints.

Fossa(e), a depressed or hollow area; a cavity.

Fusiform, spindle-shaped; shaped like a round rod tapered at the ends.

G

Gastro-, stomach.

Gastrointestinal, stomach and intestines.

Genia-, origin.

Genital(s), L., belonging to birth. Refers to reproductive structures; loosely, the term refers to the external genitals of either sex.

Glia, see neuroglia.

Glomerulus, a small cluster of vessels or nerve endings, as in the glomerulus of the kidney.

Glosso-, tongue.

Glyco-, sweet, pertaining to sugar or carbohydrate, e.g., glycogen (starch), glycoprotein (sugar-protein complex).

Glycoprotein, an organic compound consisting of carbohydrate and protein.

Glycosaminoglycan, a long chain of double sugars (disaccharides) connected with a nitrogen-containing group (amine); *glyco* = sugar, *glycan* = polysaccharide. Previously termed mucopolysaccharide. Proteins combined with glycans are temed proteoglycans.

Gomphosis(es) (gom-PHO-sis), bolting together. See joint classification, structural.

Gray matter, brain and spinal cord substance consisting largely of neuronal cell bodies, glia, and unmyelinated processes. Collections of gray matter are generally called nuclei or centers.

Groove, a linear depression in bone.

H

Hallucis, genitive form of hallux.

Hallux, great (first) toe.

Hand, the most distal part of the upper limb. The skeleton of the hand consists of the carpus, metacarpus, and phalanges. It joins with the forearm at the wrist (radiocarpal) joint.

Haustra(e), sacculations of the large intestine held in tension by longitudinal bands of smooth muscle (taeniae).

Haversian system, a cylindrical arrangement of bone cells and their lacunae, named after C. Havers, a 17th-century anatomist; the central tubular cavity, the Haversian canal, contains vessels. Seen in compact bone.

Head, that part of the body supported by the skull and superior to the first cervical vertebra.

Hem-, blood.

Hematocrit (he-MAT-oh-krit), the measurement of red blood cell volume in a tube of centrifuged blood; the tube itself is called a hematocrit tube.

Hematoma (hee-mah-TOE-ma), *hemat* = blood, *oma* = tumor or swelling. A collection of blood under the skin, fascia, or other extracellular membrane.

Hematopoiesis (hee-mah-toh-po-EE-sus), blood cell formation; occurs in the bone marrow and, in early life, in the liver and spleen; blood cells include red blood corpuscles and white blood cells.

Hemi-, half.

Hemopoiesis (hee-mo-po-EE-sus), see hematopoiesis.

Hemorrhage (HEM-or-ij), bleeding; escaping of blood from blood vessels into the adjacent tissues or onto a surface.

Hemorrhoid, a varicose dilatation of a vein that is a part of the superior/inferior rectal (hemorrhoidal) plexus of veins.

Hemosiderin (hee-mo-SID-er-in), storage form of iron.

Heparin, a glycoprotein present in many tissues that has anticoagulation ("blood thinning") properties.

Hepat-, liver.

Herniation, a protrusion through a wall or wall-like structure.

Heterogeneous, varied, as in a mixture of nonuniform elements.

Hg, mercury (chemical symbol).

Hiatus, an opening.

Hindfoot, that part of the foot posterior to the transverse tarsal (talonavicular and calcaneocuboid) joints.

Hip, the coxal bone; the region of the hip (coxal) joint.

Histamine, a nitrogenous molecule whose effects include contraction of smooth muscle and capillary dilatation.

HIV, human immunodeficiency virus.

Homogeneous, of uniform quality.

Hydroxyapatite, Ca (PO) (OH), a mineral or inorganic compound that makes up the mineral substance of bone and teeth. A very similar structure is found in nature outside the body.

Hyper, excessive.

Hyperplasia, increased number of normal cells.

Hypertonia, increased muscle tension; increased resistance to stretching of muscle.

Hypertrophy, increase in size of muscle.

Hypo, inadequate or reduced.

Hypoesthesia, reduced sensation.

Hyster-, uterus.

I

-iasis, condition, presence of.

Ileo-, ileum of the small intestin.

Ilio-, ilium of the coxal (hip) bone.

Immuno-, refers to the immune system or to some activity or part of that system.

Immunosuppression, suppression of immune (lymphoid) system activity; also called immunodepression.

Impinge, to have an effect on something; contact, irritate, strike.

Infarction (in-FARK-shun), an area of dead tissue caused by interruption of the blood supply to the tissue.

Infection, the invasion of body cells, tissues, or fluids by microorganisms, usually resulting in cell or tissue injury, inflammation, and immune response.

Inflammation, a vascular response to irritation, characterized by redness, heat, swelling, and pain; may be acute or subacute (lasting more than two weeks, or chronic).

Infra-, under.

Inhibition, restraint or restraining influence.

Injury, anatomic disruption at some level of body organization in response to an external force (e.g., blunt, penetrating, electrical, radiation, thermal).

Innate, inborn, congenital.

Innervation (in-nerv-AY-shun), provision of one or more nerves to a part of the body.

Innominate, unnamed. First applied to the coxa (hip bone) by Galen; first applied to the artery by Vesalius.

GLOSSARY

Integument, the skin.

Inter-, between; e.g., interscapular, between the scapulae.

Intercalated, inserted between.

Interface, surfaces facing one another; to face a surface.

Interstitial, interstices, interstitium, interspaces of a tissue; between two or more definitive structures.

Intima, innermost part.

Intra-, within; e.g., intracellular, within a cell.

Intramembranous ossification, see ossification.

Intravenous, within a vein.

Intrinsic, part of a specific area and not extending beyond that area (e.g. thumb, hand, foot). Muscles that arise (originate) and insert within the hand region are known as intrinsic muscles (of the hand).

Investing, surrounding or enclosing.

Isometric contraction, a contraction that involves muscle contraction without bone movement, so that the muscle maintains the same apparent length. Fibril shortening in such a contraction is offset by the inherent elasticity of the myofascial tissue.

-itis, inflammation. Term does not specify the cause of inflammation; therefore, it does not mean infection, but may refer to the inflammation induced by or associated with an infection.

J

Jejuno-, jejunum of small intestine.

Joint classification, functional; joints are classified according to the degree of movement, i.e., immovable, partly movable, freely movable. Immovable joints are called synarthroses, partly moveable joints are called amphiarthroses, and freely movable joints are called diarthroses. Immovable joints may be fibrous (sutures, gomphoses) or cartilaginous (synchondroses). Synovial joints are not normally immovable. Partly movable joints may be fibrous (syndesmoses) or cartilaginous (symphyses). Freely movable joints are always synovial. Synovial joints are limited in their motion by joint architecture and ligaments, but within those limitations, they are normally freely movable. See also syn-.

Joint classification, structural; joints are classified according to the material that makes the joint, i.e., fibrous, cartilaginous, bony, synovial. Fibrous joints are further classified as sutures (thin fibrous tissue between flat bones of the skull), syndesmoses (ligamentous sheets between the bones of the forearm and leg), and gomphoses (fibrous tissue between tooth and bony socket). Cartilaginous joints are further classified as synchondroses (hyaline cartilage between the end and shaft of developing bone) and symphyses (fibrocartilaginous discs between bones, as between vertebral bones and between the pubic bones). Bony joints are fibrous or cartilaginous joints that have ossified over time (synostoses). Classification of synovial joints can be seen in Plate 22.

Jugular (JUG-yoo-lar), referring to the neck or a neck-like structure. Specifically refers to the vein(s) of the neck so named.

K

Kary-, nuclear.

Keratin, a sclero-protein that is insoluble and fibrous. It is the principal constituent of the outer layer of stratified squamous epithelia in skin (stratum corneum; see Plate 19), hair, and tooth enamel (Plate 138).

Kerato-, outer skin.

-kine, movement.

Kinin (KY-nin), a polypeptide (short protein) that influences reactions, such as antigen-antibody complexes.

Knee, the region between the thigh and the leg.

Kyphosis (ky-PHO-sis), humpback. Anatomically, a curve of the vertebral column in which the convexity is directed posteriorly; in orthopaedics, it is an excessive curvature of the thoracic vertebrae.

L

Labium(i), lip, or any fleshy border.

Labyrinthine (laba-RINTH-een), interconnecting, winding, as in an interwoven series of passageways.

Lacerum (lahss-AYR-um), an irregular aperture or opening.

Lacuna(e), a cavity or lake-like pit.

Lacrimal, referring to tears.

Lamella(e), a thin, plate-like structure; may be circular, as seen in the Haversian system of bone.

Lamina(e), layer.

Laryngo-, larynx.

Latency, inactivity. Usually a period between moments of activity.

Latent, see latency.

Leg, that part of the lower limb between the knee joint and the ankle joint.

-lemma, covering or sheath.

Lepto-, slender.

Leptomeninges, pia mater and arachnoid combined.

Levator, a lifter; an elevator.

Lieno-, spleen.

Ligament, fibrous tissue connecting bone to bone; also a peritoneal attachment between organs.

Lip-, pertaining to lipids; fat; triglyceride (composed of glycerol and three fatty acids).

-listhesis, slip.

Lith-, stone.

Lithotomy, removal of a stone.

Lordosis, a curve of the back seen in the cervical and lumbar regions in which the convexity is directed anteriorly; anatomically, it refers to any curve of the back so described; orthopaedically, it is an excessive curve as described.

Lumen(ina) (LEWM-un), a cavity, space, or tunnel within an organ.

Lunar, referring to the moon. **Semi-lunar**, half-moon-shaped.

Lymphatic, refers to the system of vessels concerned with drainage of body fluids (lymph).

Lymphoid, refers to the tissue or system of organs (lymphoid or immune system) whose basic structure is lymphocytes and reticular tissue.

Lymphokine (LIM-fo-kine), a product of activated lymphocytes that enters into solution and influences immune responses, generally by enhancing destruction of antigen.

-lysis(es) (LYE-sis), destruction or dissolution.

M

Macro, large, as in macromolecule.

Magnum, great.

-malacia, softening, as in demineralization of bone; changes in matrix of a tissue resulting in a loss of turgor or fibrous quality.

Mamm-, breast.

Manual, referring to the hand.

Manus, hand.

Mastication (*masticate*, to chew), the act of chewing.

Mastoid, breast-shaped.

Matrix(ices) (MAY-trix), fluid or viscous background or ground substance, often apparently amorphous and homogeneous, often colorless. A variety of organic compounds and minerals may be dispersed within.

Meatus (mee-AYT-us), an opening or passageway.

Media, middle.

Mediastinum(a) (mee-dee-ahs-TY-num), middle partition; the partition or septum between the lungs in the thorax.

Mediate, influence.

Mediator, an influential substance; a substance that acts indirectly but influentially in a reaction or in inducing a reaction.

Medulla, inner part.

Medusa, the radiating, contorted, dilated venous network bulging out on the surface of the anterior abdominal wall of chronic sufferers of portal vein hypertension/obstruction has been given the name caput Medusae (head of the Medusa). In Greek mythology, Medusa was one of the Gorgon sisters, characterized as winged monsters with heads of snakes in place of hair. When a person looked at one of them, he was turned to stone. Medusa was the only mortal Gorgon. In offering service to his tyrant king, Perseus pursued Medusa and cut off her head (which, though detached, still had the power to turn onlookers into stone). Perseus presented the head to the vile king and his men, who, upon casting their eyes on the snake-covered head, promptly turned to stone. Perseus then became king.

Mega-, big, great, as in megakaryocyte.

-megaly, enlargement.

Menin-, refers to meninges.

Meninges, dura mater, arachnoid, and pia mater coverings of the spinal cord and brain, and the first part of cranial and spinal nerves.

Ment-, referring to the chin, as in mental foramen.

Mesenchyme (mesenchymal), embryonic connective tissue, often with plenipotentiary cells.

Mesothelium(a) (meezo-THEE-lee-um), the epithelium lining the great (closed) body cavities, e.g., pleura, peritoneum, and pericardium. It is of mesenchymal origin, not ectodermal, and has different properties from classical epithelia.

Meta-, change.

Metr-, uterus.

Micro, small, as in microtubule.

Microorganism, one of a group of organisms including bacteria, viruses, fungi, protozoans, and other microscopic life forms.

Micturition, urination; discharge of urine outside the body.

Mineralization, the process of mineral (calcium complexes) deposition, especially in bone formation and remodeling as well as formation of teeth.

mm, millimeter.

mm Hg, millimeters of mercury. A pressure-measuring system in which the open end of an evacuated (vacuum) graduated cylinder (tube) is placed in a container of liquid mercury. The pressure of the atmosphere or fluid pressing on the mercury will push the mercury up the cylinder. The distance the mercury moves up the tube is measured in mm Hg and reflects the pressure imposed.

Modulate, to induce a change.

Modulator, a controlling element or agency.

Mortise, a recess that receives a part, as the talus fits into the recesses of the tibia and fibula.

Motor, referring to movement; with respect to the nervous system, refers to that part concerned with movement.

Mucosa(e) (mew-KOS-ah), a lining tissue of internal cavities open to the outside. Epithelial/gland cells secrete a mucus onto the free surface of the lining, which consists of epithelial lining cells, glands, and underlying connective tissue and nerves/vessels; it may have a thin layer of muscle.

Mucous, referring to mucus.

Mucus, a secretion of certain glandular cells, composed largely of glycoproteins in water, forming a slime-gel consistency, thicker than serous fluid.

Multi-, many.

Muscularis (muss-kew-LAHR-is), a layer of muscle.

Musculoligamentous, consisting of muscle and ligament.

Musculoskeletal, consisting of muscle, bones, ligaments, tendons, fasciae, and joints.

Musculotendinous, consisting of muscle and tendon.

Myelin (MY-eh-lin), compressed cell membranes of Schwann cells in the PNS and oligodendrocytes in the CNS, arranged circumferentially, in layers, around axons. Composed of cholesterol, components of fatty acids, phospholipids, glycoproteins, and water.

Myelo-, marrow; usually refers to spinal cord.

Myelopathy, neurologic deficit resulting from spinal cord injury or disease.

Myo-, referring to muscle.

Myoepithelium(a), contractile epithelial cells. Usually located at the base of gland cells, with tentacle-like processes embracing secretory cells. Particularly prominent in sweat, mammary, lacrimal, and salivary glands.

Myofascia, skeletal muscle ensheathed by vascular and sensitive fibrous connective tissue.

Myoglobin, the oxygen-containing, pigment-containing protein molecule of muscle.

Myosin, the principal protein of muscle associated with

contraction and relaxation of muscle cells.

Myriad, a great number.

Myx-, mucus.

N

Naso-, nose, nasal.

Neck, that part of the body inferior to the head and superior to the first thoracic vertebra and confluent with the shoulders, upper back, and upper chest; cervical region.

Necrosis (neh-KRO-sis), a state of cellular or tissue death.

Nephro-, kidney.

Neuro- (NOO-roh), nervous, referring to nervous structure or the nervous system.

Neuroglia (noo-ROHG-lee-ah), nonconducting support cells of the nervous system, including the astrocytes, oligodendrocytes, ependyma, and microglia of the CNS, and Schwann cells and satellite cells of the PNS.

Neurologic (neurology), concerned with disorders of the nervous system. Also refers to nerve/neuronal disorders seen in a clinical setting.

Neuron (NOO-ron), nerve cell.

Neurovascular, refers to nerve(s) and vessel(s), as in neurovascular bundle.

Nociceptor (no-see-SEP-tur), a receptor for pain.

Nucha- (NOO-kaw), posterior neck.

O

Oculus(i), eye.

-oid, having similar form; -like.

-oma, tumor.

Omni-, all, universally; e.g., omnidirectional, in all directions.

Ooph-, ovary.

Ophth-, eye.

Optic, relating to the eye.

Or-, mouth.

Orb, sphere, round structure.

Orbicular, rounded, circular.

Orbit, the bony cavity containing the eyeball.

Orchi-, testis.

Organelle(s) (or-gan-ELL), small functional structures within the cell cytoplasm.

Os-, bone.

Oscilloscope, an instrument that permits visualization of baseline and waves of changes in electrical voltage.

-osis, condition or state of; e.g., arthrosis is a generic term for a condition of a joint.

Osseous, relating to bone.

Ossification, endochondral, formation of bone by replacement of cartilage/calcified cartilage.

Ossification, intramembranous, formation of bone directly from osteoprogenitor cells in embryonic connective tissue (mesenchyme) or in fibrous tissue adjacent to fractured bone. There is no intermediate stage of cartilage formation or replacement.

Ossification, primary center of, the principal center of bone formation in the diaphysis or center of developing bone.

Ossification, secondary center of, a satellite center of ossification, as in the epiphysis.

Osteo-, bone.

Osteoblastic, referring to bone-forming cells (osteoblasts).

Osteoclastic, referring to bone-destroying cells (osteoclasts).

Osteoid (OSS-tee-oyd), bonelike; nonmineralized bone.

Osteoprogenitor, a primitive cell that has the potential, when stimulated, to become a bone-forming cell (osteoblast).

-ostomy, operation that makes an artificial opening.

Ovale, oval.

Oxy-, oxygen.

P

Pachy-, thick.

Pachymeninx, dura mater.

Palpable (PAL-pah-bul), touchable; by touch.

Palpate, to touch or feel (a common clinical technique).

Palsy, weakness.

Para-, alongside.

Parenchyma (pah-REN-keh-ma), the functional substance of an organ.

Paresis, weakness caused by incomplete paralysis.

Parietal (pah-RY-et-all), referring to a wall or outer part.

-pathy, disease.

Ped-, foot.

Pedal, foot.

Pedicle, footlike process; narrow stalk.

Pedo-, child.

Peduncle, a narrow stalk, specifically, masses of white matter in the CNS.

Pelvic girdle, the two coxal (hip) bones.

Pelvis(es), the ring of bone consisting of the two coxal (hip) bones and the sacrum and coccyx.

-penia, deficiency or decrease.

Penicillar, resembling a painter's brush or pencil.

Pennate, feather-shaped.

Peri- around.

Perichondrium (paree-KOND-ree-um), the fibrous envelope of cartilaginous structures (except articular), containing blood vessels, fibroblasts, and chondroblasts (immature cartilage cells).

Perineal, referring to the region inferior to the pelvis.

Periodontal, around a tooth.

Periosteum (paree-OS-tee-um), the fibrous envelope surrounding bone, containing osteoprogenitor cells, osteoblasts, fibroblasts, and blood vessels, serving as the life support system of bone.

Peripheral, away from the center, near or toward the periphery.

Peristalsis (paree-STAHL-sis), waves of coordinated and rhythmic muscular contractions in the walls of a cavity or tubelike organ, induced by hormones or other secreted factors and by nerves of the autonomic nervous sustem.

Peroneal, the lateral (fibular) side of the leg.

Perpendicular, refers to a plane at right angles (90 degrees) to an adjoining plane.

Pes, foot.

GLOSSARY

Pes anserinus, goose's foot. Refers to the tendons (sartorius, gracilis, and semitendinous) that collectively insert on the medial proximal tibia.

Petrous (PEET-russ), rocky or like a rock.

-pexy, fixation or suspension.

Phagocyte, a cell that takes up cell fragments or other particulate matter into its cytoplasm by endocytosis. Phagocytes with a segmented nucleus are called polymorphonuclear leukocytes (neutrophils); mononuclear phagocytes (of the monocyte-macrophage lineage) are known by several names, depending on their location—e.g., macrophages, monocytes of the blood, histiocytes of the connective tissues, Kupffer cells of the liver, alveolar (dust) cells of the lung, microglia of the cental nervous system. Many cells that are phagocytic under certain circumstances are not called or considered phagocytes.

Phagocytosis (fago-site-OH-sus), the taking of fragments or other particulate matter into a cell.

Phlebo-, vein.

-physis(es), growing part.

-pial, referring to pia mater.

Pinocytosis, cellular ingestion of fluid.

Pituitary (archaic), referring to mucus.

-plasia, referring to development or growth.

Plasm-, referring to the substance of some structure, e.g., cytoplasm (cell substance).

-plasty, surgical correction.

Plenipotentiary, having the capacity to develop along a number of different cell lines. Undifferentiated mesenchymal cells, pericytes, and certain other cells have such capability.

Pneumo-, air.

P.N.S. or **PNS**, peripheral nervous system, consisting of cranial and spinal nerves and the autonomic nervous system.

Pole (polar), either extremity of an axis, as in south and north poles of the Earth. Also refers to processes of a neuron (e.g., unipolar).

Pollex, thumb. **Pollicis**, genitive form.

Poly-, many or multi-.

Polymodal, with many modalities; polymodal receptors are responsive to several different stimuli.

Portal circulation, veins that drain a capillary bed and terminate in a second capillary or sinusoid network, as in the hepatic portal vein and the portal system of the hypophysis.

Post-, back of, after, posterior to.

Pre-, in front of, anterior to.

Precursor, a forerunner, whose existence precedes something that is formed from it.

Pro-, in front of.

Procerus (pro-SE-russ), long, slender muscle.

Process, bony, a projection sticking out from a surface.

Process, neuronal, an extension of a neuron, containing cytoplasm/organelles and limited by a cell membrane. A neuronal process (dendrite or axon) is part of a living cell.

Procto-, rectum.

Prolapse, the sinking down or displacement of a structure, such as the sinking of the uterus into the vagina.

Propria (prohp-ree-ah), common.

Protein, a chain of amino acids of varying length.

Proteoglycan, chain of disaccharides (carbohydrates) connected to a core of protein; a binding material.

Proteolytic, causing digestion or breakdown of protein.

Protuberance, a projection, or something sticking out from a surface.

Proviral, refers to viral DNA that has been integrated into the DNA of the host cell.

Pseudo (SOO-doh), false. In anatomy or medicine, having the appearance of one structure or phenomenon but not, in fact, being such a structure or phenomenon.

Pterygoid (TAYR-ee-goid), winglike.

-ptosis, falling, drooping.

Pulp, a soft, spongy tissue, often vascular.

Pyel-, pelvis.

Pyo-, pus.

Q

Quad-, four.

Quadrant, one-quarter of a circle.

Quadrate, four-sided; rectangular, usually square.

R

Radi-, ray.

Radiculitis, inflammation/irritation of a nerve root.

Radiculopathy, nerve root deficit characterized by change in the deep tendon (stretch) reflex, sensory loss (objective numbness), and muscle weakness.

Radix, root.

Ramus (RAY-mus), a branch.

Ratio, a fixed relationship or proportion between two things; e.g., 1:4 means that there is 1 unit for every 4 other units.

Recto-, rectum. See also procto-.

Reflux, backward flow.

Renal, referring to the kidney. See also nephro-.

Repolarization, an electrical change in excitable tissue away from neutral polarity, e.g., increasing polarity from 0 millivolts to −90 millivolts.

Residue (REZ-ih-doo), the material left over after processing and extraction of other parts.

Reticulum(a), a small network.

Retro-, back, behind, posterior; opposite of antero-.

Retroperitoneum, the area posterior to the posterior layer of parietal peritoneum. It lies anterior to the muscles of the posterior abdominal wall and includes the kidneys, ureters, abdominal aorta and immediate branches, inferior vena cava and immediate tributaries, pancreas, and ascending and descending colon.

-rhaphy, suture.

Rotundum, round.

S

Salpingo-, referring to uterine tubes.

Salpinx, uterine tube.

Sarco-, flesh.

Scavenger cell, see phagocyte.

Schwann cell, cell of the peripheral nervous system that provides myelin for some and a membranous covering for all axons. A line of Schwann cells forms a tube for axonal regeneration after axonal injury.

Sciatica, pain in the buttock radiating to the foot via the posterior and/or lateral thigh and leg; it follows the distribution of the sciatic nerve, and therefore is assumed to be irritation of that nerve or its roots (radiculitis).

Scoliosis (sko-lee-OH-sis), any significant lateral curvature of the vertebral column. Some degree of lateral curvature is seen in most spines, probably related to use of the dominant hand.

-scopy, inspection or examination of.

Sebum, the oil lying on the surface of skin, secreted by sebaceous glands (see Plate 19).

Secondary sex characteristics, anatomic and physiologic changes occurring as result of increased sex hormone secretion (testosterone in the male, estrogen in the female); these characteristics develop at puberty (generally at 11–14 years of age). In the male, they include growth of body hair, change in voice due to change in laryngeal structure, increased skeletal growth, increase in size of external genitals, functional changes in internal genitals, and changes in mental attitude. In females, they include enlargement of breasts, change in body shape due to skeletal growth and distribution of body fat, and maturation of internal and external genital structures.

Secretion, elaboration of a product from a gland into a duct, vessel, or cavity. See excretion.

Sella, saddle.

Sellar, saddle-shaped.

Semi-, half or partly.

Sensitive, responsive to stimuli, eliciting an awareness of touch, pressure, temperature, and/or pain; innervated.

Sensory, referring to sensation (e.g., touch, perception of temperature, vision).

Septum(a), a wall or an extension of a wall; a structure that separates.

Serosa (sir-OH-sa), lining tissue of cavities closed to the outside, consisting of a layer of squamous or cuboidal cells and underlying connective tissue.

Serotonin, a nitrogenous molecule with many functions, including acting as a neurotransmitter, inhibitor of gastric secretion, and vasoconstrictor.

Serous, watery; see serum.

Serum, any clear fluid; also blood plasma less plasma (clotting) proteins.

Sesamoid, pea-shaped. Generally refers to small bones of the hand and foot. The largest sesamoid bone is the patella. These bones are formed within the tendons or ligaments at points of stress.

Sharpey's fibers, fibrous bands of ligaments, tendons, and/or periosteum inserting directly into bone.

Shoulder, the part of the body where the upper limb is joined to the trunk; specifically, the shoulder joint and surrounding area, including the upper lateral scapula and distal clavicle (acromioclavicular area).

-sial, referring to saliva.

Sinus(es) (SY-nuss), a cavity or channel. A venous sinus is a large channel, larger than an ordinary vein; an air sinus is a cavity.

Sinusoid, sinuslike; usually refers to thin-walled, porous vessels in glands. Generally slightly larger than capillaries, sinusoids vary in their structure depending on their location.

Soft tissue, any tissue not containing mineral, e.g., not bone, teeth. Generally refers to myofascial tissues.

Soma, the body; the body wall.

Somatic, referring to the body or body wall, e.g., the cell body of a neuron (soma); in organizational terms, contrasted with viscus or viscera (organs containing cavities).

Spasm, rapid, violent, involuntary muscle contraction, usually resulting in some contortion of the body part experiencing the spasm.

Spheno- (SPHEE-no), shaped like a wedge; refers to a triangular-shaped structure that comes to a thin edge on one side.

Sphincter, a concentric band of muscle surrounding a narrowed cavity or passage.

Spindle, a structure that is round and tapered.

Spinosum, spiny or spinelike.

Spleno-, spleen. See also lieno-.

Spondyl-, vertebra.

Squamous, platelike, thin. Generally refers to flat, thin epithelial cells.

Stenosis (sten-OH-sis), narrowing.

-stomy, hole or opening.

Stratified, layered; having more than one layer.

Stria, stripes or parallel markings.

Styloid (STYL-oyd), having the form of a pointed spike or pillar.

Sub-, under.

Subchondral, under cartilage; specifically, the bone adjacent to articular cartilage.

Subcutaneous (sub-kew-TANE-ee-us); under the skin.

Subdural, under the dura; between the dura and the brain or spinal cord.

Supra-, above.

Suture (SOO-chur), a type of fibrous or bony junction characterized by interlocking, V-shaped surfaces, as in the skull.

Swallowing, deglutition.

Sym-, see syn.

Symphysis(es) (SIM-fih-sis); see joint classification, structural.

Syn- (SIN), together, with, alongside.

Synarthrosis(es) (sin-arth-RO-sis); see joint classification, functional.

Synchondrosis (sin-kon-DRO-sis); see joint classification, structural.

Syndesmosis(es) (syn-des-MO-sis); see joint classification, structural.

Synostosis(es) (syn-os-TOH-sis); see joint classification, structural.

Synovial (sih-NOH-vee-ul), refers to a viscous fluid similar in consistency to uncooked egg white. This fluid and the membrane that secretes it line freely movable joints (synovial joints), bursae, and tendon sheaths.

Synthesis(es), formation of a structure from smaller parts; integration of parts.

T

Taenia(e) coli, strips of longitudinal muscle in the mus-

GLOSSARY

cularis externa of the large intestine (excluding the rectum and anal canal).

Tarsal, tarso-, the ankle.

Tendinitis, inflammation of a tendon.

Tendinous (TEN-dih-nuss), referring to tendon.

Tendon, fibrous tissue connecting skeletal muscle to bone or other muscle. May be cord-like or sheet-like (aponeurosis).

Thigh, that part of the lower limb between the hip joint and the knee joint.

Thorax, the region between the neck and the abdomen.

Thrombosis(es), a condition of clots or thrombi within a vessel or vessels.

Thrombus(i), a clot within a blood vessel, obstructing flow.

-tomy, incision.

Tone, normal tension in muscle, resistant to stretch.

Torso, the part of the body less the limbs and head; the trunk.

Transcriptase, an enzyme (polymerase) directed by DNA to facilitate synthesis of a single strand of RNA that is structurally complementary to a strand of DNA.

Transcriptase, reverse, a polymerase (enzyme) directed by RNA to facilitate synthesis of a single or double strand of DNA that is structurally complementary to a strand of RNA. In HIV infection of cells, RNA-directed reverse transcriptase makes possible the transcribing of viral RNA sequences into double-stranded DNA; this is then integrated into the host cell's DNA. The combined DNA is called proviral DNA.

Trauma, an anatomic or psychic response to injury.

Trochanter, a large process. Specifically, two processes of the upper femur.

Trochlea (TROHK-lee-ah), a pulley-shaped structure.

-trophic, relating to nutrition.

Truss, a collection of members (beams) put together in such a way as to create a supporting framework.

Tubercle (TOOB-er-kul), a rough, small bump on bone.

Tuberosity (toob-eh-ROSS-eh-tee), a bump of bone, generally larger than a tubercle, smaller than a process.

Tunica, referring to a coat or sheath; a layer.

Turcica (TUR-sih-kah), Turkish, as in sella turcica (Turkish saddle).

U

Uni-, one. A unicellular gland is a one-cell gland.

Unibody, of one body; a structure with parts integrated into one unit.

Unit, a single thing or quantity; the basic part of a complex of parts.

Urogenital, referring to structures of both the urinary and genital (reproductive) systems.

Urogenital diaphragm, a layer in the perineum consisting of the sphincter urethrae and deep transverse perineal muscles and their fasciae. Also called the deep perineal space.

V

Vacuolation (vac-u-oh-LAY-shun), formation of small cavities or holes; part of a degenerative process in cartilage during bone development.

Vacuum, a space devoid of air, with, therefore, no pressure. In the relative sense, decreased pressure in the thoracic cavity during inspiration represents a partial vacuum, drawing air from a space with air of higher pressure.

Varix(ces), an enlarged, tortuous (twisted) vessel.

Varicosity(ies), an enlarged and irregular-shaped, highly curved (tortuous) vein(s). Most often seen in superficial veins of the lower limbs and the testes/scrotum.

Vas(a), vessel.

Vasa vasorum, vessel that supplies a larger vessel.

Vascular, referring to blood or lymph vessels or to blood supply.

Vasorum, of the vessels.

Ventricle, a cavity.

Vessel, a tubelike channel for carrying fluid, such as blood or lymph.

Vestibule, an entranceway, cavity, or space.

Villus(i), a fingerlike projection of tissue, as in the intestinal tract or placenta.

Viral, relating to a virus.

Virion, a single virus, also called a virus particle, consisting of genetic material (DNA or RNA) and a protein shell (capsid).

Virus, one of a group of extremely small infectious agents, consisting of genetic material and a protein shell. A virus is not capable of metabolism, and thus requires a host to replicate. On attachment to a surface molecule on a cell membrane, a virus particle is enveloped by the cell membrane and brought into the cytoplasm, thus infecting the cell.

Viscous, a fluid or semi-fluid state wherein molecules experience significant friction during movement.

Viscus(era), an organ with a cavity in it.

Vomer, a plowshare-shaped structure.

W

White matter, a substance of the brain and spinal cord consisting of largely myelinated axons arranged in the form of bundles or tracts. It appears white in the living or preserved brain.

Wrist, the carpus, the region between the forearm and hand.

Wrist drop, a condition in which the extensors of the wrist are weak or paralyzed. The wrist cannot be extended and therefore the wrist "drops" when one attempts to hold the hand horizontally or vertically upward. This condition is usually the result of radial nerve denervation.

X

Xeno-, foreign.

Xero-, dry.

Z

Zygapophysis(es) (zi-gah-POFF-ee-sis), an articular process of a vertebra; also a joint between vertebrae (zygapophyseal articulation). Such synovial joints may be called facet joints. See also facet.

Zygo- (ZY-go), referring to a yoke or union; joined.